MANITOU, SARATOGA OF THE WEST

Sponsored by

The Mineral Springs Foundation of Manitou Springs

Previously sponsored by

El Paso County Medical Society Alliance

First edition 1980
Second edition (revised) 1998

ISBN 0-9663939-0-2

PRINTED BY GOWDY-PRINTCRAFT PRESS, INC.
COLORADO SPRINGS, COLORADO

MANITOU, SARATOGA OF THE WEST

by

Sharon A. Cunningham

Illustrations by

Anne Kircher Dye

The town clock is located on a triangle of land formed by Manitou, Canon, and Lafayette Avenues. It was given to Manitou by Jerome Wheeler in 1890. Hygeia, the Greek goddess of health, stands above the timepiece. She is the daughter of Aesculapius, the god of medicine. According to Greek mythology, her particular function is to maintain the health of a community.

FOREWORD

In 1975, the El Paso County Medical Society Auxiliary established a committee to research the medical history of the county. The research project was divided into three sections: Manitou Springs, the tuberculosis era, and early physicians. This publication covers the early medical history of Manitou Springs. It is not a scientific study; it is a historical account of the development of Manitou Springs as a spa. Only some of the physicians who hung their shingles in Manitou are discussed here. These are the doctors listed in local libraries, and those whose descendants were able to share information about their lives. There were others about whom little background could be obtained; and there were those who came to Manitou for their own health and practiced here while spending a summer.

The first two printings of this book were financed by the El Paso County Medical Society Auxiliary (presently Alliance). The profits helped to fund the design and building of the Manitou display in the Medical Heritage Hall at the Colorado Springs Pioneers Museum. This display is available for public viewing.

The Mineral Springs Foundation of Manitou Springs has made funds available for this revised edition. It is the hope of the author that profits from this book be used by the Mineral Springs Foundation in their work to preserve and promote the springs as well as the history and culture of Manitou's past.

ACKNOWLEDGEMENTS

Most of the information for this publication was obtained from Pikes Peak Regional Library, Special Collections and Archives of The Colorado College Library, Manitou Springs Public Library, Denver Public Library, Manitou Springs Historical Society, Colorado Historical Society, Colorado Springs Pioneers Museum, Colorado Medical Society, El Paso County Medical Society, and El Paso County Medical Society Alliance. The help and cooperation given to me by the personnel of these institutions are greatly appreciated.

I wish to thank the following individuals who were most willing to share their memories, photographs, and expertise: Carolyn Abrahams, Belvadene Boyd, Guy Boyd, Katie Broe, Cloyd L. Brunson, Jean M. Campbell, Dale Clarke, Shirley Copp, William Copp, Rhoda Cordry, Basil B. Creighton, Mary Forest Creighton, Alfred H. Dwyer, Albert L. Forde, Edwina Forde, Kathleen Gamblin, Ed Liby, Verni Martz, Libby Pitman, Elsie Schueler, Louise Bos, Lynn Lane, Mike Stanton, Edmond Van Doren, Rhoda Davis Wilcox, Lester L. Williams, and Glenn H. Zimmer.

I am very grateful to my editor, Dee Fischer.

To my family and friends, I give special thanks for their patience and understanding.

S. A. C.

The springs that bubbled in natural basins along the banks of the Fontaine qui Bouille at the foot of Pikes Peak naturally attracted the Indians. Mountain tribes traveling Ute Pass, and plains tribes following the banks of the stream, now called Fountain Creek, were awed by these effervescent pools, as well as by the towering Pikes Peak, the strange rock formations of the Garden of the Gods, the shimmering streams, and the abundance of game. All of this was certainly a paradise and surely a gift from the universal god who controlled nature — a gift so revered that the area was sacred to the Ute, Comanche, Kiowa, Cheyenne, Arapaho, and Sioux nations. Anyone entering this neutral ground would lay down his arms and pass in peace.

The first Indian visitor must have quickly realized the unique qualities of the volatile waters. Not only did the waters quench his thirst, but they also alleviated stomach problems caused by his diet of game meat, wild berries, and other natural foods of the area. The waters also seemed to lessen his internal discomfort resulting from the stress of the last battle or the pressure of being a good hunter. The cool waters on a summer day invited a swim. Afterward, the Indian felt clean and refreshed, and he noticed an ease in his stiff, rheumatic limbs. His old war wounds were less painful. After drying, he felt his skin softened and relieved of itching. Such experiences soon convinced the Indian that these were truly medicine waters.

In his book *Manitou, The Gitche Spirit of the Red Man*, L. Edwin Smith related an enchanting myth of the accidental discovery of the healing powers of the medicine springs:

> An old Indian chief, sick and despairing of life, wandered aimlessly away from his people, caring not whither his faltering steps led him. Exhausted, his strength spent and his will-power gone, he stumbled and fell head-long into a spring of bubbling, cold water. Momentarily revived by the shock, he partially raised himself, when a mystic spell possessed him. Resting there on his hands, with staring eyes he looked down into the transparent waters where he saw reflected the image of his God — the

Spirit Manitou. Drinking deep draughts of the spirit-charged water, the chief soon regained his strength, and shortly afterwards brought his people to dwell in this beautiful, spirit-blessed valley. The old chief proclaimed that the "spirit of healing dwelt in the waters," and his people "drank the spirit waters to drive their ills away." Thus they came to worship the Great Spirit which dwelt below these waters.[1]

The reputation of the medicine waters spread rapidly among the tribes. Another legend told of a young warrior who came seeking the safety of this sequestered land and the curative powers of the well-known waters. He was racked with fever and near death from severe battle wounds and was in need of nourishment, rest, and a long drink of water. A Manitou travel folder ended the story as follows: "He flung himself, weak and spent and almost unto death, upon the soothing earth beneath the shade of the towering trees, and drinking deep of the revivifying waters, murmured the name of his Great Spirit — Manitou."[2] The warrior found himself healed of his wounds and ready for battle again.

A party of Ute Indians is traveling the Ute Trail through the Garden of the Gods.

The derivation of the term "Manitou" was established by Mr. Smith, who traced the origin of the word to the ancient Algonquin Indians that inhabited the eastern United States. He found that before the European missionaries arrived the Indians had no specific god. They attributed the strange happenings of nature to occult manifestations. The missionaries put into their minds the idea that there was a greater force controlling the universe — a god, a supreme being — a force not necessarily evil. The Algonquin Indians then began to believe that a spirit dominated the forces of nature, and they called it "Manitou." This idea of a spirit spread west as the Indians became more mobile and began to communicate their ideas.

The Indians felt a need to repay the great spirit, Manitou, who caused these medicine waters to boil up from his great mixing bowl deep within the earth. Evidence of their gifts of beads, wampum, knives, moccasins, animal hides, cloth, and clothing was found by the early Spaniards, white trappers, traders, hunters, and explorers. Those who dared intrude in the sacred valley related the secret of the medicine waters. The word spread rapidly throughout the country.

Thomas Jefferson completed the purchase of the Louisiana Territory in 1803. The acquisition stirred excitement, curiosity, and a need to explore the Rocky Mountains. One of the early explorers was Zebulon Montgomery Pike, who brought with him the first physician to enter the Territory of Colorado, Dr. John Hamilton Robinson, a young man of twenty-four at the time of the expedition. The doctor was present November 15, 1806, when Pike first viewed the mountain which was given the name Pikes Peak.

When General James Wilkinson gave Pike his orders to explore the southwestern part of the Louisiana Purchase, he informed Pike that Dr. Robinson had volunteered to  accompany the group. His saddle bag was his office. It contained four kinds of drugs — opium, from the poppy, was given to relieve pain and inflammation; quinine, a derivative of Jesuit's bark, was a cure for malaria and was used as a tonic; heart problems were treated with digitalis, or the leaves of foxglove; and calomel, a form of mercury, was used as a laxative, a diuretic, an antiseptic, and a treatment for syphilis. Besides the drugs, he carried a lancet, an instrument used to rid a patient of bad blood that might be the cause of infection. [3]

Dr. Edwin James, a botanist, geologist, and surgeon attached to the expedition led by Major Stephen H. Long, came in 1820. He made the first successful attempt to climb Pikes Peak, and the mountain's name was changed for a period of time to James Peak. Dr. James's climbing party set up base camp near the bubbling springs, thus enabling him to observe the action of the waters:

> The *boiling spring* is a large and beautiful fountain of water, cool and
> transparent, and aërated with carbonic acid. . . . The water of the spring
> deposits a copious concretion of carbonate of lime which has accumulated
> on every side, until it has formed a large basin overhanging the stream;
> above which it is raised several feet. This basin is of a snowy whiteness,

and large enough to contain three or four hundred gallons, and is constantly overflowing.

The spring rises from the bottom of the basin with a rumbling noise, discharging about equal volumes of air and water, probably about fifty gallons per minute; the whole kept in constant agitation. The water is beautifully transparent; and has a sparkling appearance, the grateful taste, and the exhilarating effect, of the most highly aërated artificial mineral waters. [4]

Denver Public Library, Western History Department
Dr. Edwin James

As more and more white men began to move through the valley, the Indians feared that to see would mean to seize, and that they would be moved away from their sacred grounds and the medicine waters. There is a legend that the Indian braves vowed vengeance against the first paleface who dared enter their paradise. A white man was captured and sentenced to torture by the chiefs of several nations camped in the neutral grounds at the time. Firewood was prepared and the torture was about to begin when an aged Shoshone chief declared that, by the law of the tribes, the stranger was safe on these grounds. To take his life would be the greatest of all sacrileges. [5]

Perhaps because of the old chief s words, Colonel A. G. Boone and his two sons were allowed to spend the winter of 1833 near the springs, unmolested. Colonel Boone had heard of the healing powers of the medicine waters and brought his two sons, who were in poor health, hoping they would be cured. This first white health seeker was the grandson of the well-known Daniel Boone of Kentucky.

In 1842, Brevet Captain John C. Fremont was drawn by the towering mountain and renamed it Pikes Peak. He found the springs, drank the waters, and analyzed the contents, determining that the bubbling, boiling appearance of the springs was caused by the escaping gases. For a few years the springs were called "Fremont Soda Springs."

Capt. Fremont . . . has furnished the following analysis of an incrustation with which the water of this spring has covered a piece of wood; and, though probably not a fair test, it will afford the reader some idea of its mineral properties:

Carbonate of lime	92,25
Carbonate of magnesia	1,21
Sulphate of lime ⎫	
Chloride of calcium ⎬	23
Chloride of magnesia ⎭	
Silica	1,50
Vegetable matter	20
Moisture and loss	4,61
. . . .	100,00 [6]

Rufus B. Sage, a trapper, adventurer, and journalist, also passed through the area in 1842. He told why the early French missionaries named the creek the Fontaine qui Bouille ("boiling fountain"):

This name is derived from two singular springs, situated within a few yards of each other at the creek's head, both of which emit water in the form of vapor, accompanied with a hissing noise — the one strongly impregnated with sulphur and the other with soda.

He also described evidence of Indian offerings:

The Arapahoes regard this phenomenon with awe, and venerate it as the manifestation of the immediate presence of the Great Spirit. They call it the *Medicine Fountain* and seldom neglect to bestow their gifts upon it whenever an opportunity is presented.

These offerings generally consist of robes, blankets, arrows, bows, knives, beads, moccasins, &c., which they either throw into the water or hang upon the surrounding trees. Sometimes a whole village will visit the place for the purpose of paying their united regard to this sacred fountain. [7]

George F. Ruxton, who explored the area in 1847, described his visit in a book entitled *Adventures in Mexico and the Rocky Mountains*. He is believed to be the first author to actually refer in writing to the Indian spirit that controlled nature as "Manitou."

The Indians regard with awe the "medicine" waters of these fountains, as being the abode of a spirit who breathes through the transparent water, and thus, by his exhalations, causes the perturbation of its surface. The Arapahós [*sic*], especially, attribute to this water-god the power of ordaining the success or miscarriage of their war-expeditions; and as their braves pass often by the mysterious springs, . . . they never fail to bestow their votive offerings upon the water-sprite, in order to propitiate the "Manitou" of the fountain, and ensure a fortunate issue to their "path of war." [8]

He went on to tell the famous legend of how there came to be a bitter and a sweet spring in this sacred valley. Two Indians, one a Comanche and the other a Shoshone, met at a spring to quench their thirst. The latter had been successful in his hunt, so before he took a drink of the water from the spring, he gave thanks to the great spirit. The unsuccessful Comanche allowed himself to be filled with jealousy and drowned the Shoshone in the spring. The spirit of nature arose in anger, punished the Comanche by death, and caused the water of this spring to be bitter. In memory of the Shoshone warrior, the spirit of nature struck a flat rock which rose above the stream and created a round basin filled with bubbling, cool, sweet water. The bitter spring was referred to as the Shoshone Spring, and the Navajo Spring produced the sweet water. [9]

Local History Collection, Pikes Peak Library

This photograph shows the Navajo Spring as the early Indian and white visitors knew it. The basin where the spring originated was located on a flat boulder above Fountain Creek. The soda water trickled over the boulder into the stream below. Indian women enjoyed bathing in the stream here as the ingredients of the water had a soothing effect upon their skin.

Fitz Hugh Ludlow, an author and traveler, passed through the area of the springs in the late 1860s. In a book published in 1870, *The Heart of the Continent*, he wrote:

> These springs are very highly estimated among the settlers of this region for their virtues in the cure of rheumatism, all cutaneous diseases, and the special class for which the practitioner's sole dependence has hitherto been mercury. When Colorado becomes a populous State, the springs of the Fontaine qui Bouille will constitute its spa. In air and scenery no more glorious summer residence could be imagined. The Coloradian of the future, astonishing the echoes of the Rocky foot-hills by a railroad from Denver to the Springs, and running down on Saturday to stop over Sunday with his family, will have little cause to envy us Easterners our Saratoga as he paces up and down the piazza of the Spa Hotel, mingling his full-flavored Havana with that lovely air, quite unbreathed before, which is floating down upon him from the snow-peaks of the range. [10]

To the Indian, the valley of boiling waters was sacred. To the hunter, it was abundant with a great variety of game. For the trapper, the area provided quantities of beautiful hides. The mystery of the new territory invited explorers and adventurers. As this new land grew more familiar to the nation as a whole, it became necessary to connect East and West with a better means of transportation. This need brought two men to the area on a surveying trip for the Kansas Pacific Railway, and, with their arrival, the entire environment changed. These men were General William Palmer and Dr. William Bell.

Dr. Bell came to St. Louis from England in 1867 to continue his study of medicine, but found himself responding to the call of adventure — the adventure being the railway survey expedition led by General Palmer. The only assignment available was that of photographer, so Dr. Bell quickly learned photography. When the physician originally assigned to the party left the group, Dr. Bell was able to fill that position for the remainder of the trip. This venture brought these two ambitious men into a lifelong friendship and a financial partnership.

While looking for an advantageous southwestern route for the railway, General Palmer and his expedition found themselves exploring the plains below Pikes Peak in the year 1868. Although this section of country was not approved for the Kansas Pacific route, General Palmer realized that the area was in a direct line with a possible railroad leading south out of Denver to Mexico — his first conception of what became the Denver and Rio Grande Railroad.

The fame of the sacred valley of the red man naturally lured General Palmer and Dr. Bell to investigate the well-known soda springs while in the vicinity. They followed the shrubbery-lined cattle trail to the spot, and Dr. Bell immediately fell in love with the beautiful valley of the Fontaine qui Bouille. He recalled the day in 1868 when he and General Palmer first visited the valley. After taking in the surrounding beauty, they decided to plunge into the big basin of the main spring. This is how Dr. Bell described the experience in a speech given to the Village Improvement Society:

The immense escape of gas produced a novel and most invigorating sensation. It caught you in the small of the back and lifted you up with great force; and the action of the gas on the skin was similar to that of the gas on the throat as you drink it. It was very stimulating and you rapidly became as red as a lobster. [11]

With his background in medicine and knowledge of the popularity of the spa in that day, Dr. Bell could picture a health resort villa here to take advantage of what nature offered so abundantly.

Special Collections and Archives
The Colorado College Library

General William J. Palmer

Local History Collection,
Pikes Peak Library

Dr. William A. Bell

General Palmer, impressed with the climate, springs, and scenery, could also see the possibility of an exclusive spa in the valley as well as a city on the plains below. The seeds were sown, ideas were triggered, and the railroad was the key to bringing the population. The visions of General Palmer and Dr. Bell, of two cities with dual purposes, soon became a reality.

The Kansas Pacific Railroad was completed to Denver on August 15, 1870. The Denver and Rio Grande Railway Company was organized in the fall of that year. Land for the first seventy-six miles of railway was acquired and construction began on the railroad south out of Denver by July of 1871. Meanwhile, in June 1871, the Colorado Springs Company was formed. The company purchased the land for the city on the plains and the resort villa sites in El Paso County along Monument and Fountain Creeks. Capital for the land acquisitions came from General Palmer's friends in the East and from English supporters of Dr. Bell.

The first stake was driven on July 31, 1871, for the city that was to be built on the larger tract of land. The city was laid out by the Colorado Springs Company in generous proportions with the hope of attracting only those citizens of high moral character. Three months later, on October 21, 1871, the railroad line was complete to the new city of Colorado Springs.

Dr. Bell intended that the villa which became Manitou would cater to the wealthy from Europe and from the east coast of the United States. In 1872, this villa was plotted on the 640 acres surrounding the springs in the valley along Fountain Creek and laid out to take advantage of the lay of the land and the beauty of the area. Dr. Bell described how it was done:

> We then laid out the town site in accordance with the views we had as to the future of the place. The streets and roads were adapted to the contour of the ground; the lots were made of large size and of necessity irregular, and were mostly intended for villa sites. At that time the present city of Colorado Springs was a treeless and bare waste of plain and was not attractive. In the valley through which the Fountain flows we pictured with the eye of the future, lovely villas surrounded by mountains and greenery. [12]

In 1872, this article concerning the founding of Manitou appeared in *Out West*, the first newspaper of the region:

> Mr. Blair, landscape gardener, who has just returned from Chicago, and Mr. Nettleton, resident engineer of the Colorado Springs Company, are engaged in laying out a small town close to the Soda Springs at Manitou. The town will lie in a hollow on the left side of the present road, just before the Shoshone Spring is reached. About 150 lots are being laid out, 75 for business purposes, 25 feet by 100 feet, and 75 for residence lots with double the frontage. Between 400 and 500 Villa sites have been laid out, the locations having been made with the utmost care so as to give each its individual beauties whilst contributing to the beauty of the whole scene. Directly the laying out of the little town is completed, Mr. Blair will put on a large force to supplement the natural beauties of the glen: roads and paths will be constructed, bridges built, and rustic seats placed in appropriate spots. The new hotel is rapidly approaching completion, and furniture for it has already been ordered, part of it being on the way. It is anticipated that the hotel will be ready for the reception of visitors by the 15th of next month. [13]

The villa had to have a name. The first one chosen was La Font, but this was not satisfactory to the town supporters as it did not create the image such a place deserved. References to the word "Manitou" as the Great Spirit in Ruxton's *Adventures in Mexico* and Henry Wadsworth Longfellow's *Hiawatha* seemed relevant, and so the new health spa of the West was named.

At this point it is of interest to know more of the background of the man responsible for developing the valley of the mineral springs into the grand watering place that it became at the turn of the century. An individual of lesser energy could never have accomplished what William Abraham Bell did during his eighty-one years of life. Besides being the founder of Manitou, he was involved in many of the ventures of General Palmer and was very active in securing the funds for these endeavors. Together they founded the Denver and Rio Grande Railroad, the Mexican National Railroad, and the Colorado Fuel and Iron Company. Dr. Bell laid out townsites and resorts along their railroad lines. Durango, Colorado, is one of these towns. On his own, he was responsible for the Manitou Park Resort, just eighteen miles up Ute Pass from Manitou, and a cheese factory in the Wet Mountains. If he wasn't traveling to England to procure capital needed for his projects, he was moving about Colorado to keep track of his railroad, mining, and land businesses. Rhoda Davis Wilcox, in her biography of Dr. Bell, tells of a time when this active individual became ill. His good friend, General Palmer, commented that it was "good to see him quiet for a change." [14] Dr. Bell didn't have time to be quiet, nor did he have time to practice medicine.

Dr. Bell graduated in 1861 from Trinity College Cambridge with honors in natural science, and he received his medical training at St. George Hospital in London. He came to St. Louis at the request of his father, who was a distinguished London physician, to attend a lecture series on homeopathic medicine. It was at this time that Dr. Bell joined General Palmer's survey party. When this adventure ended, he returned to England to report to his father what he had learned at the meetings and to write a two-volume account of his travels, entitled *New Tracks in North America*. Besides discussing the commercial benefits of North America, he gave colorful descriptions of the wildlife, the flora, the health-giving climate, and the Indians. His fascination for the West and his enthusiasm for adventure brought him back with the financial support of his friends.

Denver Public Library, Western History Department

Dr. and Mrs. William A. Bell

Dr. Bell married Cara Georgina Whitmore Scovell in England in 1872 and brought her to his beloved valley and his "pet project" — that of building a health resort. Cara's vivacious energy and her charming personality equaled William's, and her support was of benefit to him. In their beautiful home, Briarhurst, built along the Fontaine qui Bouille, they raised four daughters and a son, and from this home they conducted the development of the "Saratoga of the West," the "Baden-Baden of America," the "Gem of the Rocky Mountains" — Manitou.

Courtesy, Colorado Historical Society

Briarhurst, the home of Dr. and Mrs. Bell, was always open to friends. The original structure burned in 1886 and the second Briarhurst was completed in 1888. Today it is called Briarhurst Manor, a chef-owned and operated "landmark restaurant" and an elegant setting for weddings and other festive occasions.

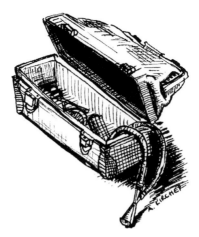

A physician and conscientious health seeker from London, England, appeared in Manitou at the end of 1874. Dr. Samuel Edwin Solly (1845–1906) came at the persuasion of his friend, Dr. Bell, with a most impressive background in the treatment of lung, nasal, and throat disease. Like Dr. Bell, he was the son of a prominent London physician, a surgeon whose work on the human brain was a medical classic. Dr. Solly received his early education at Rugby and his medical schooling at St. Thomas Hospital Medical College, and he took special training as a resident physician in an insane asylum. He graduated in 1867 from the Royal College of Surgeons in London and took over his father's practice.

The doctor became a renowned expert in the field of climatology and its use as a treatment for pulmonary disease. This interest began when he was eighteen and was suffering from lung disease which forced him to travel to health resorts on the Riviera, and in Egypt, Switzerland, and America. He had firsthand experience with both public and private sanitariums as curative measures for tuberculosis. His personal acquaintance with specialists in tuberculosis and his associations with his father's protégés in the field of laryngology enhanced his training in these areas of medicine.

Dr. Solly was forced to leave England at the age of thirty because of another break in health. He accepted the advice of Dr. Bell and came to Manitou with his young wife, immediately fitting in with the large English element that had settled here. They had two daughters and lived in the resort village for a brief time. After the death of his first wife, Dr. Solly moved to Colorado Springs where he continued to practice medicine.

Dr. Solly was generous with his expertise and published many articles and essays in the fields of tuberculosis and climatology. He belonged to many societies concerned with tuberculosis, science, and medicine, among which were the El Paso County Medical Society, the Colorado Medical Society, and the American Medical Association. Public spirited as well, Dr. Solly was enthusiastic about the health resorts of Manitou and Colorado Springs, and he prepared publications which helped advertise the area as a spa. [15] He realized the need for a first-class hotel in Colorado Springs to adequately house the tourists and invalids — the result was the Antlers Hotel. The monument to his theories of tuberculosis treatment was the establishment of Cragmor Sanatorium [16] in Colorado Springs.

While in Manitou, Dr. Solly continued his study of climatology and at the same time developed an interest in the mineral springs. He was the first to examine the contents of the springs and their use in the treatment of diseases. An analysis of the Manitou springs done by Professor O. Loew, here with the Wheeler expedition, was used by Dr. Solly in his study. His work was published in a pamphlet entitled *Manitou, Its Mineral Waters and Climate.* The following review appeared in the *Colorado Springs Weekly Gazette* in 1875:

> Dr. Solly first takes up Prof. Loew's analysis of the Manitou mineral waters made in 1874, and reduces it from a form too scientific for the ordinary understanding, to another more simple and convenient, ... Dr. Solly then goes into a history of the use of mineral waters as remedial agents, tracing back to remote ages. He shows what particular forms of disease different kinds of mineral waters are efficacious in, and makes comparisons between the Manitou waters and those of Europe, better known than ours. . . . He further writes descriptively of Manitou, Colorado Springs, and of the climate thereof, and compares our mountain climate to that of the sea-coasts resorted to in Winter by consumptives and other invalids; showing why our mountain air is in many important respects a more potent remedial agent in the winter season than that of the sea at the same time of year.
>
> Dr. Solly's book will be a valuable adjunct in the great work of bringing before the outside world the claims of this section of country as a place of resort for tourists, and a home for invalids peculiarly afflicted. It is extremely well written and bears evidence of research and thought. It is by all odds the best and most interesting work on the subject we have read, and we urge our friends who desire to assist in the work of building up Colorado generally, and Southern Colorado in particular, to send copies of it to Eastern people "where it will do the most good." [17]

At the time Dr. Solly wrote his pamphlet there were six analyzed springs: the Navajo, Manitou Soda, Shoshone, and Ute Soda along Fountain Creek; and the Little Chief and Ute Iron along Ruxton Creek. All contained carbonic acid and carbonate of soda but varied in the other ingredients. The doctor felt it necessary to understand the mineral contents of the springs so that they could be used to their best advantage. He believed that an ailment should be chronic in nature and have reached a point of no improvement. Then the waters could be used as a remedy because of their ready solubility and high dilution, causing the minerals to be absorbed into the tissue at a slower rate than with artificial combinations. This allowed the body more time to adjust to its metamorphosis.

In his booklet, Dr. Solly categorized the springs in three groups. In the first group were found the carbonate of soda waters which had carbonic acid and soda as their chief action — the Navajo, Manitou Soda, and Ute Soda. The second group included purging carbonate of soda waters in which the carbonic acid and soda were modified by sulfates of soda and potash — the Shoshone and the Little Chief. The third set of springs produced the ferruginous carbonated soda waters where the action of the carbonic acid and soda were modified by carbonate of iron — the Ute Iron and the Little Chief.

Dr. Solly found that soda was the most active ingredient in the Navajo Spring. Its soda content was the strongest of the first group; thus it was the best representative of the soda waters. The rocks surrounding the pool were white with soda and striped with green and peacock blue as a result of its mineral deposits. Dr. Solly placed great importance on the curative powers of the Navajo Spring through both drinking and bathing. Some of the cases that were reportedly improved by drinking from the Navajo were catarrh (inflammation of the mucous membrane) of the stomach and bowels, gout, rheumatism, pleurisy, dropsy, gallstones, kidney problems, obesity, chronic bronchial catarrh, chronic enlargement of the liver and spleen, and chronic dyspepsia.

He believed that through carefully supervised soda water baths many health problems could be relieved. The temperature of the water needed to vary according to the problem being treated and the physical condition of the patient. Cold water was used only for patients in better health. According to Dr. Solly, the soda content of the spring had a softening effect upon the skin and relieved itching. The carbonic acid allowed the person to take a hotter bath than normal, leaving him with a sense of invigoration. He felt that bathing relieved gouty and rheumatic swelling, improved the making of blood, and encouraged the assimilation of food. Drinking and bathing simultaneously was a great benefit in some cases.

Special Collections and Archives
The Colorado College Library

Dr. Samuel E Solly

The Shoshone was a good example of the "purging" springs. This spring was bitter because of its mineral content. The rocks around it were encrusted with a yellowish deposit caused by the presence of sulfates in its water. In addition to carbonate of soda, it contained sulfate of soda and sulfate of potash which, according to Dr. Solly, gave this spring its purging powers. He felt that "six or even four tumblers (8 oz. each) taken in the day insured a fluid evacuation every morning."[18] He also gave illustrations which helped establish the medical uses of this spring.

In a patient, the subject for many years of habitual constipation with occasional attacks of hepatic congestions, accompanied by feverishness and slight jaundice, and who came under my care while passing an hepatic calculus, as soon as the acute attack had passed, I recommended the drinking of six glasses of Shoshone daily, commencing with two before breakfast, and found that a good bilious evacuation was procured daily. The appetite, which was previously capricious, became regular and the general health good. At first, a teaspoonful of Glauber's salt was added to the first glass, but after a few days this was discontinued, and by the patient taking a little more of the water at meals, sufficient effect was produced by the water alone. In a case of hemorrhoids occuring [*sic*] in a person of full habit of body somewhat inclined to free living, I found a few glasses of Shoshone ward-off a return of the symptoms and secure an easy action of the bowels daily. In a case of icterus (jaundice) of several weeks standing, arising probably from catarrh of the gall-bladder, accompanied by very considerable enlargement of the liver, with much languor and vertigo and the passage of hard, clay-colored stools, after taking podophyllin and rhubarb for eight days, he discontinued them and took Shoshone water alone, six glasses a day. His improvement advanced, his bowels acting freely twice a day, and at the end of the three weeks and a-half he was under treatment, his liver had returned to its normal size, his skin was clear, his bowels were natural, and he felt strong and well.

These illustrations, I think, show that in most cases of functional derangement of the liver, in preventing attacks of gall-stone in hepatic dyspepsias and their consequences, such as hemorrhoids, etc., a safe remedy can be found in the *Shoshone*.[19]

The third group of springs referred to in Dr. Solly's pamphlet were those containing carbonate of iron in addition to carbonic acid and carbonate of soda — the Iron Spring and the Little Chief located on Ruxton Avenue along Ruxton Creek. The rocks surrounding these waters resembled reddish chunks of iron. Dr. Solly found these waters to be beneficial in cases of chronic alcoholism and anemia.

Dr. Solly felt that, along with the medicinal waters of the springs, this area offered other advantages to the health seeker, such as the climate, altitude, pure mountain air, and scenery:

There is probably no climate in the world where outdoor life is so thoroughly enjoyable through every season of the year as that of Colorado. This fact is of special force as regards the *winter* season, when we consider how few *bracing* health resorts there are in the United States that do not suffer from the disadvantage of excessive cold.

Manitou lies in a valley amidst the mountains at an elevation of six thousand three hundred and seventy feet; but it is unlike other mountain health resorts, which are either, as in Switzerland, hemmed in on all sides by mountains, or like those lying on the slopes of the Pyrenees, overlooking a country covered with growing crops, woods, towns, and water. Manitou, though hills gradually rising to the dignity of the mountains protect it on three sides from the winds, while their gentle slopes do not shut out the sun, yet opens out at its northeast extremity onto the great plains themselves, thus reaping the benefit of so vast an open space filled with an atmosphere highly rarefied and dry and, above all, free from all the impurities which emanate from decaying vegetation, swampy soil, or crowded cities. The mountains shelter Manitou from the winds and dust storms, which make life upon the plains during the winter and early spring almost impossible to the delicate invalid, while their height is not great enough to shut out the sun; so that even in the shortest days of winter there are at least six hours of warm sunshine to tempt the invalid to exercise. [20]

The spa was a fad and a trend in medicine of the times, a trend which can be traced back to the ancient Greeks, who were the first to develop an organized form of medicine. They considered the mineral springs an important treatment for certain health problems. The Romans also made use of the springs found in their country — particularly those at Naples and Thermopolis — and in the lands they conquered, such as the hot springs of Bath, England. The Bible tells of early belief in the medicinal effectiveness of the pool of Bethesda. The 1800s saw a renewed interest in the healing powers of mineral waters, and as a result the spa became popular throughout the world. The Germans did more than any other nationality to develop the technique of bathing for medicinal purposes. Hydrotherapy is the name given to the treatment of disease through the internal and external use of water.

It must be remembered that the miracle drugs, such as sulfa and penicillin, and the medical technology of today did not exist, and the physician had to rely on what was available. The spa offered the mineral waters which contained ingredients that were beneficial in cases chronic in nature. Faith in the medicinal powers of the waters was an attitude which aided the curative effects of the spa. The relaxed atmosphere of these health resorts was also an important part of the treatment.

The European spas to which Manitou was compared were Spa, Belgium; Baden-Baden, Nauheim, Ems, and Pyrmont in West Germany; Vichy, France; St. Moritz, Switzerland; and Carlsbad, Czechoslovakia. Those most popular in the United States at the time of Manitou's fame were Hot Springs, Arkansas, and Saratoga, New York — Manitou's nickname, "Saratoga of the West," came from the latter. Because Colorado was rich in ground minerals, it was natural for these minerals to appear in the springs found in many parts of the state. Health resorts could be found at Glenwood Springs, Idaho Springs, Steamboat Springs, Pagosa Springs, and Canon City. Manitou was the first health resort in the Territory of Colorado.

General Palmer and Dr. Bell realized that, in order to compete with the other health resorts, they would need to launch an advertising campaign that would lure the health seekers to their western spa. Through the efforts of General Palmer's office in New York, Dr. Bell's European contacts, the Denver and Rio Grande Railway Company, the Colorado Springs Company, and doctors who came to this area, the word was spread very effectively that Manitou was a health resort of unsurpassed beauty and equal in quality to any other spa in either Europe or North America.

Prior to 1872, Manitou was one of nature's "jewels in the rough," but man's skill polished this gem and made it worthy of its surroundings. General Palmer and Dr. Bell designed it as an oasis for the seekers of health, pleasure, and culture. In a comparatively short period of time, the footprints of these visitors replaced the hoofprints of the deer and elk as the early game trails became romantic paths which led from spring to spring. The Indian teepees and the shacks of the early settlers were replaced by fine hotels, cottages, shops, and stately homes. This toy-like village, nestled in a valley at the foot of Pikes Peak at an altitude of 6,340 feet, offered its visitors a rare combination of invigorating climate, pure air, unparalleled scenery, unlimited outdoor activities, excellent hotels, pleasant associations, conscientious physicians, and, of course, the mineral springs — and so it was advertised.

Local History Collection, Pikes Peak Library

Dr. L. L. Williams Collection

A massive advertising campaign celebrated the scenic beauty, the climatic advantages, and the medical benefits of Manitou, the Saratoga of the West. Advertisements were designed to entice permanent residents, health seekers, and tourists.

It took a great deal of effort for a health seeker to travel to Manitou. An individual from Boston, for example, who suffered from a stomach ailment and was stiffened by rheumatism, decided to seek the relief and relaxation of a spa. He read an ad for the health-giving waters of Manitou, Colorado, and chose to spend the summer at this resort. The invalid selected a trunk line headed west out of Boston to Chicago, where he boarded the Union Pacific for a fast run to Denver; at this point he connected with the Denver and Rio Grande Railroad for the seventy-five mile trip to Colorado Springs. For every train arriving in Colorado Springs, there was a railroad or an electric car connection to Manitou, just six miles or twenty minutes away. For this trip the fare was twenty-five cents. Before these modern means of transportation, there were three stages a day to transport travelers to Manitou.

A glorious trip it was as the train pointed its engines west toward the gap in the hills that rose to the majesty of Pikes Peak. On his right, the invalid saw the waters of the rushing stream reflecting in the warm sunlight. Everywhere he saw the wild clematis gracefully clinging to trees and boulders. Wildflowers added a touch of color to the unbelievable sight which gave the health seeker a renewed spirit. Suddenly the railroad reached the crest of a hill and below appeared the lazy resort village.

The invalid stepped onto the platform of the English cottage-style depot of the Denver and Rio Grande Railroad, and was met by the clamor of the hotel runners telling him of the advantages of their lodges. While trying to make a choice, he looked toward the village with its impressive hotels dominating the scene. The architecture of these buildings gave him the feeling that comfort, luxury, and hospitality would be found within their walls.

This health seeker registered at the Cliff House and, after a refreshing bath and a rest, he was ready to dine in the fine restaurant on the first floor. He enjoyed a gourmet dinner complete with a glass of Ute Chief Table Water, and he ended his meal with a cool glass of Original "Manitou" Ginger Champagne. He quickly learned that it was fashionable after each meal to stroll to the springs for a sip and a chat with fellow visitors.

The variety of activities available to him each day included tennis, billiards, bowling, and excursion trips to the Garden of the Gods and the Cave of the Winds, through Cheyenne Canyon, and, of course, up Pikes Peak. Each evening a hop, a concert, or even gambling was offered. The invalid inquired as to the location of the bath house and the name of a reliable physician. He was set to start restoring his health, both physically and mentally, and was surely ready to enjoy every minute of his recovery.

Colorado Springs Pioneers Museum

Local History Collection, Pikes Peak Library

The beauty and charm of the Denver and Rio Grande Railroad Depot greeted the tourists and health seekers as they arrived in Manitou by train, creating a pleasant first impression of the spa. As many as five trains daily brought visitors to Manitou.

The large hotels were a predominant feature of the town. The fine architecture of these buildings was complemented by beautifully landscaped grounds. The hotels offered the health seekers a fashionable, leisurely home during their stay, graciously providing every convenience to meet the needs of all members of the family, and they were the center of activity during the season.

Courtesy, Colorado Historical Society

The Manitou House was the first large hotel built by General General Palmer and Dr. Bell. Forty-eight of its fifty-eight rooms were filled on opening day, August 13, 1872. This two-story colonial structure was furnished throughout in first-class style, and it offered the visitor a quiet and sequestered environment. The Manitou House was located near the site of the present Seven Minute Spring pavilion. It burned in 1903.

The Mansions, Dr. Bell's second hotel in Manitou, opened in June 1875. Located just west of the present town hall on Manitou Avenue, the hotel was situated on its own ten-acre park which included two drilled mineral springs. Its elegance was unsurpassed in the state. One advertisement, in S. K. Hooper's book, Manitou, *described The Mansions as a hotel for those "who enjoyed the whirl and excitement of a fashionable watering place." It offered fine food in the Dutch Room, concerts and hops in the popular Saratoga Room, and a variety of outdoor sports. This building was destroyed by fire.*

The 110-room Barker Hotel is located at 819 Manitou Avenue, across from the Shoshone Spring. It opened its doors in 1891, and was advertised in Hooper's Manitou *as the "favorite of the quiet, wealthy class who come for a genuine rest, and who enjoy the solid comfort to be found there, which resembles that of their well ordered and luxurious homes." It was the first hotel to have a hydraulic elevator. For a period of time it was known as the Navajo Hotel. In 1979, this building was listed on the National Historic Register. In order to be so listed, its name was changed back to its original name, the Barker Hotel. The building has been restored and made into an apartment complex for senior citizens.*

Stewart's Commercial Photographers, Inc.

The Cliff House rests against a cliff at the mouth of Williams Canyon, at 306 Canon Avenue. The original two-story building on this site was constructed in 1872 and was known as The Inn until Edward E. Nichols purchased it in 1873 and changed the name to the Cliff House. Under the ownership of Mr. Nichols and his family, it grew from a 20-room boarding house to a 265-room hotel that changed with the times.

The Cliff House was advertised to be the largest and best hotel in the state of Colorado. The owners provided their guests with every convenience. Two concerts were performed daily in the music room, and printed programs were distributed each morning informing the guests of the music scheduled for the day. The main dining room seated three hundred, and each evening meal was a formal affair. "The Ordinary" was the dining room set aside for children and their governesses. Guests at the Cliff House enjoyed electricity, baths, elevators, billiard rooms, and a barber shop. Outside there were lawn tennis courts, croquet grounds, and a large playground for the children.

Clemma McIlrath, in her "History of Cliff House," told how the bellboys would fill bottles and glasses with the soda water from the Manitou Soda Spring just across the street and carry them to the hotel every night at 9:00. The sparkling water was passed around at the close of the evening concert so that the guests could "drink to each other's health before retiring."

It was an impressive list of guests who enjoyed the pleasures the Cliff House had to offer. Some of the notable names that registered were Katharine Lee Bates, John D. Rockefeller, Henry Ford, P. T. Barnum, General Ulysses S. Grant, Thomas Edison, Clark Gable, Theodore Roosevelt, J. Paul Getty, and Robert Louis Stevenson.

Today the Cliff House is being restored to its Victorian-era elegance and will house fifty-six guest rooms and suites. It has been renamed The Cliff House Inn.

Two of the three Iron Springs Hotels were situated in Engelmann Canyon at the top of Ruxton Avenue close to the Ute Iron Spring and near the Pikes Peak Cogway Depot. An ad in Facts *magazine dated July 2,1898, boasted that this hotel had the "longest passenger elevator in the world which commences at the foot of the front stairway and runs clear to the top of Pikes Peak."*

This photograph is of the second Iron Springs Hotel, built in 1885 by the Gillis Brothers. It contained sixty-five rooms and was the first to be lighted by electricity. It was heated with steam, and it offered excellent cuisine, electric call bells, baths, tennis, and billiards. It was advertised in Hooper's Manitou *to be par excellence as a "resort for invalids, or for those who like a quiet and elegant place of resort." To add to the pleasure of this resort, a casino was built in 1891 for dances and concerts. It was located on the bank of Ruxton Creek opposite the hotel.*

When the second hotel burned, the casino became the third Iron Springs Hotel, or Château. A fire destroyed part of the Château in 1961. It was completely rebuilt to house a melodrama, containing a bar and dining facilities.

The original Iron Springs Hotel was built on what is now Pilot Knob by Dr. William Strickler, who arrived in 1869 to become one of the first physicians in El Paso County. He purchased land in the canyon which included the iron springs and the hotel site. The hotel, built to take advantage of the beautiful scenery, was located such that it was protected from the high winter winds, thus making it a fine winter resort. It burned in 1882.

In addition to the hotels, rooming and boarding houses, cottages, and apartments were available to the visitors. In 1889 it was estimated that these lodges housed three- to four thousand visitors at one time. The different accommodations offered rates to fit every purse. A publication dated 1891 listed these rates.[21]

Cliff House	$3.00 to $4.00
Barker House	$3.00 to $4.00
Manitou House	$3.00 to $4.00
Iron Springs Hotel	$3.00 to $4.00
The Mansions	$3.00 to $4.00
Sunny Side House	$2.50 to $3.50
Hotel Ruxton	$2.50 to $3.00
Revere House	$2.00 to $3.00
Norris House	$2.00 to $2.50
Mineral Springs Hotel	$2.00
Oak Cottage	$2.50 to $4.00
Grand View	$2.50
The Arlington	$2.00 to $3.00

"Red Crags"

LAURIE P. AND WALTER D. SAWIN, OWNERS AND PROPRIETORS

Situated on a high, sunny prominence, one mile east of, and over-looking the beautiful town of Manitou, and is intended for that class of patients who are desirous of securing first-class care, where especial attention will be given to sanitation and diet, according to individual needs. Choice Eggs, Poultry, Milk and Cream produced on the premises, supply the table.

Tubercular and all contagious diseases excluded.

Manitou Springs Historical Society

This advertisement for Red Crags appeared in an undated booklet published by the Manitou businessmen. Red Crags was purchased in 1912 by the Sawins. Like many Manitou citizens, they opened their home to health seekers, offering first-class care to patients with noncontagious diseases. Red Crags was built in 1888 or 1889 by Dr. William Bell in association with a Dr. Donaldson. Little is known about the latter other than that he was a Rough Rider with Theodore Roosevelt. They may have intended to use Red Crags as a hospital. This building still stands and has seen many owners.

The Manitou Item of May 27, 1882, reported that there were five mineral springs of note within the city — the Navajo, Shoshone, Manitou Soda, Ute Iron, and Little Chief. Six hotels and boarding cottages, six livery stables, three general stores, two drugstores, two bakeries, and a number of other stores representing "various useful trades" comprised the facilities of the town. The article also mentioned that these businesses appeared to be "profitably engaged." [22]

This photograph, taken circa 1885, looks east down Manitou Avenue with the Manitou Soda Spring pavilion in the center. The Cliff House is the large building on the left.

Facts magazine, published July 22, 1899, gave a descriptive report of Manitou's heyday. The account was based on the 1898 season, from April 15 to November 1. [23] In this year there were thirteen hotels, four churches, one elementary public school, one newspaper which was issued daily in summer and weekly during the winter, a bath house, two soda water and ginger champagne manufacturing establishments, an electric light and water plant, one sanitarium (Montcalme), and a town clock.

In 1898, there were twelve springs, with the Manitou Soda Spring, referred to as the Soda, and the Ute Iron Spring used almost exclusively. The Soda and Iron Spring pavilions were open daily from 8 a.m. until 9 p.m. Because of its central location, the Soda Spring attracted a greater number of people. Six glasses of this water were drunk each minute, 360 every hour, or nearly 5,000 each day; close to 4,000 were consumed daily at the Iron Spring. This made a reported total of 440 gallons per day, and does not take into account the large quantities of water taken away in jugs and bottles.

During this season, the railroads and electric cars brought approximately 43,800 persons to Manitou. About 6,000 of these spent from three days to four weeks in town; the remainder spent one to three days.

Dr. A. G. Lewis arrived in Manitou in 1887. In October of that year, he applied to practice medicine in Colorado, and was granted license number 873 by the Colorado Board of Medical Examiners. Dr. Lewis purchased two lots at the west end of Manitou Avenue near the entrance to Ute Pass, where in 1890 he built a $9,000 sanitarium and developed a spring on the property. The sanitarium later became the Mineral Springs Hotel.

Dr. Lewis offered his patients and visitors hot mineral baths to relieve such problems as rheumatism and stiffness brought on by their ride to the top of Pikes Peak. He believed in the benefits of drinking the mineral water but felt that the amount should be regulated by a physician.

The Mineral Springs Hotel burned on March 12, 1895.

An early travel folder published by the Manitou Business Men's Association advertised that "the ONLY and all of the mineral springs of the Pikes Peak Region are situated in the center of Manitou." [24] It was discovered by many of the businessmen that these could be drilled, and if one were found on his premises, business would benefit. Drilled springs and geysers added to those occurring naturally eventually brought the number to about fifty.

Whatever way the springs emerged, the fact is that they all came from somewhere below the surface. Chemical analysis showed they all contained a high concentration of minerals and carbonic acid, and their temperatures ranged between 43 and 56 degrees Fahrenheit. Manitou is situated in a valley surrounded by sedimentary rock formations layered by the ages, each formation composed of various mineral matter. Limestone strata underlie other rocks below the town and give the springs along Fountain Creek their calcium and sodium content as well as many other minerals. The springs along Ruxton Creek differ somewhat from those near Fountain Creek in that they percolate through iron-bearing rocks and thus contain quantities of iron.

Carbon dioxide in the atmosphere will dissolve to some extent with rain water, yielding a weak solution of carbonic acid — the substance that gives soda pop its fizz. This relatively dilute acid seeps through deep cracks and crevices of carbonate rocks, dissolving minerals and producing chemical changes that will later liberate the carbon dioxide to give a bubbly effect to the emerging springs along the creeks.

Walking from one spring to another was a fashionable, beneficial, and recommended activity for the invalids and tourists. S. K. Hooper, passenger agent for the Denver and Rio Grande Railroad, suggested that "the invalid should not be afraid of fresh air; such glorious dry air can do him no harm. A walk of five or ten minutes before breakfast, in the sunshine, or a jaunt to the Iron Springs, and a refreshing draught of its sparkling waters, will serve as a sharp and effective tonic." [25]

The famous Ute Iron Spring was located one-half mile from the junction of Manitou and Ruxton Avenues on the right bank of Ruxton Creek, below the Cog Railroad. It was the most developed of the several natural chalybeate springs (those containing salts of iron) along the creek. A summer house was built over the Iron

A stroll up Ruxton Avenue to the iron springs on a warm summer afternoon was renewing in itself, and a sip of these effervescent waters was a sure tonic for anemic blood. Tourists reported that the iron taste was not repulsive, and that after a day or two the water became a delicious drink.

This summer house was the first structure built over the Ute Iron Spring, the most popular of the chalybeate group.

The pavilion in the foreground replaced the rustic summer house of the Ute Iron Spring. Here tourists and health seekers gathered to drink the pure iron water or sip the foamy lemonade made from the effervescent liquid, and to visit with new acquaintances. The building in the background is the Iron Springs Hotel.

Additions were made to the Ute Iron Spring pavilion to keep pace with the increased number of visitors. Business was expanded to include the sale of souvenirs, and dances were held here.

This advertisement appeared in the Directory of Colorado Springs, Manitou Springs, and Colorado City *in 1886. The noncarbonated bottled iron water was recommended for relief of constipation, dyspepsia, and kidney problems, and for healthy blood. The bottling of this water was discontinued because of the unpleasant sediment that settled in the bottoms of the bottles.*

Spring in 1880. At a later date, this was replaced by a more enclosed pavilion that evolved into a modern château. Visitors enjoyed the walk up the winding road that followed the creek to the château, where they could purchase lemonade made from the highly effervescent iron waters. If one wanted to drink the pure iron water, he could walk down some steps to its source. An attempt was made to bottle these waters, but a residue that collected in the bottles ended the sales. Today this spring is capped and located inside the Iron Springs Château Dinner Theater.

7690. Famous Iron Springs Geyser, Manitou, Col.

Local History Collection, Pikes Peak Library

The Iron Spring Geyser, located along Ruxton Creek below the Ute Iron Spring, was drilled in 1910. Originally, this geyser sent water shooting into the air every thirty minutes. Today this spring gurgles quietly in its basin and the water is available to the public.

The most celebrated of the historic springs of Manitou were the Navajo and the Manitou Soda. Located in the center of town on Manitou Avenue along Fountain Creek, they were the main attraction of the Soda Springs Park that surrounded them. The park was complete with pretty bridges over the creek, winding, landscaped paths, rustic log pagodas, a charming Queen Anne style bath house, the three-story redstone and frame bottling works, and the pavilion that sold souvenirs along with lemonade made with soda water.

The Navajo once bubbled in a large basin on the south bank of Fountain Creek. It has a delightful history starting with the red men who bestowed their offerings in gratitude to Manitou, who breathed life into the medicinal waters of this spring. Mrs. H. A. W. Tabor, who came at an early date with her husband, made biscuits using the soda water. A large share of Manitou's economy was dependent on this spring as these waters were used by the Manitou Mineral Water Company to make its table water and ginger champagne. The early bath houses used water from the Navajo in their hydrotherapy.

This spring has been restored and is available to the public. The water has been piped to a fountain mounted on the back side of the Patsy's Candies building. The white mineral deposits where the Navajo originally overflowed its basin into Fountain Creek can be seen through the cracks in the flooring of the arcade area behind this building.

The half-gallon jug beside this visitor to the Navajo Spring is filled with soda water. The water was frequently carried away in such containers.

The soda water of the Navajo Spring bubbled in its natural mixing bowl to the delight of this group of elegantly dressed ladies. The gentleman is passing the community cup so that the women can enjoy a drink.

It was very common for tourists, health seekers, and citizens to fill their bottles with soda water as these ladies are doing. Two of these visitors are sipping from tin cups, attached to the basin with chains.

This view shows the Navajo Spring in the foreground and the pagoda over the Manitou Soda Spring on the opposite bank of Fountain Creek. The building on the right is the Cliff House.

Across the bridge from the Navajo Spring is the Manitou Soda Spring. From 1872 to 1885, a log pagoda graced the spring; it was replaced by a pavilion, and the rustic pagoda was moved to the Navajo Spring. The new pavilion became a popular gathering place.

Originally, a tin cup was attached to the Manitou Soda Spring basin. After the pavilion was built, young lads were hired to dip water for the visitors. They dipped metal racks which held three glasses into the soda spring, drew up the filled glasses, and passed them to anyone wishing a drink. It became an art to dip the rack so that all three glasses would fill at the same time. The tin cup or a glass full of soda water was passed from tourist to tourist and from invalid to invalid to quench thirst or to fill a prescription recommended by a physician. It wasn't until 1911 that health officials began to realize that germs could be transmitted by drinking from a common container — so the Tin Cup Law was passed, disallowing this practice. Penny paper cups were sold at the pavilion, thus ending the glamorous career of the dippers.

The water from the Manitou Soda Spring was utilized in the hydrotherapy offered in the white stucco bath house built in 1920. It still gurgles inside a fountain in the lobby of the same structure, now called the Manitou Spa Building, and is available for public use.

It is interesting to note the development that occurred at this site between 1872 and the present. The natural environment was transformed from a beautiful park to a commercial spa surrounded by cement and an arcade. An Indian legend tells of a curse of failure the red men placed on anyone who attempted to make a profit by exploiting their sacred medicine waters.[26] The truth to this legend is lacking, but the fact remains that commercialization disguised the beauty of the natural resources.

This pavilion, constructed in 1885, replaced the log pagoda of the Manitou Soda Spring.

The log pagoda was moved from the Manitou Soda Spring to the Navajo Spring when the new pavilion was built. Note the bridges and paths through the Soda Springs Park and the addition to the Cliff House on the right.

The Manitou Soda Spring pavilion became a popular gathering place for tourists and health seekers. Inside, one could purchase curios as well as lemonade made with the soda water. This pavilion, open from 8 a.m. until 9 p.m., was constantly thronged with people drinking the water. Facts magazine of July 18, 1899, reported that 4,806 glasses were consumed daily. The spring actually bubbled in its basin inside the pavilion, but for the convenience of the visitors, water was piped to the circular area in the left front of the picture.

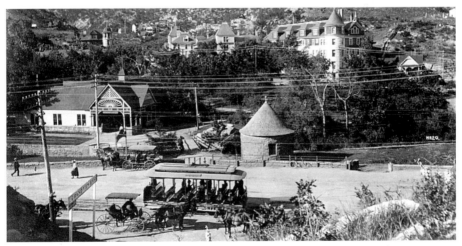

This scene looks upon the heart of Manitou, showing the Manitou Soda Spring pavilion (on the left) and the redstone structure that replaced the log pagoda over the Navajo Spring (center). Note the Cliff House rising above the dense vegetation of the Soda Spring Park.

The trolley ran from Colorado Springs to Manitou throughout the day. The turnaround for the trolley was at the intersection of Manitou and Ruxton Avenues.

37

The Manitou Soda Spring pavilion was remodeled to keep up with the changing times and the continuous flow of visitors. This structure was replaced in 1920 by the stucco building that stands today.

Across Manitou Avenue from the Barker Hotel is the Shoshone Spring, presently hidden beneath a round, stone structure. The Shoshone was also known as the Arapaho, Sulphur, or Bitter Spring. Because of its mineral content, the water had a bitter taste and was lacking in effervescence. Wild animals and cattle liked to drink the water and lick the yellowish mineral deposits that accumulated on the rocks surrounding the spring. The early physicians felt these waters had a purging effect.

This rustic log pagoda graced the Shoshone Spring, also known as the Arapaho, Sulphur, or Bitter Spring. These waters had a purging effect, and Dr. Edwin Solly felt that they were of great value where there was "torpidity of the liver." This spring had the highest radioactivity level of the 250 analyzed springs in Colorado.

Denver Public Library, Western History Department

The horse-drawn wagon travels west on Manitou Avenue past the Barker Hotel, on the left, and the Shoshone Spring pagoda, in the center. The white building in the lower right corner is the bottling shed, with the bath house next to it.

Courtesy, Colorado Historical Society

This pavilion replaced the log pagoda of the Shoshone Spring.

The western end of Manitou Avenue near the entrance to Ute Pass was the site of twelve natural and drilled soda springs as well as a drilled gusher. These springs and the adjacent property were owned by the Ute Chief Mineral Water Company, producers of table water and ginger champagne. Eight of the twelve were highly developed, while four producers were dormant, to be used if needed. Of the natural springs, the Hiawatha, the Magnetic, and the Ute Chief were the most well-known. The Ute Chief Gusher was a tourist attraction — its flow was estimated to be eight hundred gallons per minute. Indian statues erected on the property were reminders of the early tribes who first used the waters. Many of the springs and the gusher were capped or clogged by their own minerals when the water was no longer bottled.

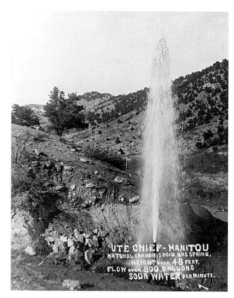

Local History Collection, Pikes Peak Library

The drilled Ute Chief Gusher, located at the entrance to Ute Pass, delighted visitors with its forty-eight-foot eruptions.

Manitou Springs Historical Society

The Ute Chief Magnetic Spring water was capable of magnetizing steel held in the water for only short periods of time. Today this spring gurgles in a well found inside the old Ute Chief bottling works.

A number of chemical analyses were made of the springs of Manitou. The first detailed study was done in 1874 by Professor O. Loew, the mineralogist with the Wheeler expedition mentioned earlier. Professor Loew analyzed six mineral springs at Manitou and for comparison he added a breakdown of the mineral waters at Spa, a famous health resort in Belgium. [27]

THE MINERAL SPRINGS AT MANITOU
In a Pint Are Contained Grains as Follows:

—OF—	Navajo	Manitou	Minnehaha [Ute Soda]	Shoshone	Iron Ute	Little Chief	Spa
Carbonate of Soda	8 3-4	3 1-4	1 2-3	6 1-5	4 1-7	1 1-17	3-5
Carbonate of Lithia	1-50	1-67	trace	trace	trace	trace	.....
Carbonate of Lime	9 1-17	7 3-4	2 4-5	7 3-5	4 1-8	5 1-4	1-2
Carbonate of Magnesia	2 1-5	1 1-2	1-2	....	1 1-50	1	1-7
Carbonate of Iron	....	trace	1-10	....	2-5	1-8	1-3
Sulphate of Potassa	1 1-7	1	trace	1-3	1-2	1-2	1-14
Sulphate of Soda	1 1-4	1 1-3	3-4	2 3-5	2 1-5	3 3-5	1-25
Chloride of Sodium	2 3-4	2 2-3	1	3	2 1-5	3 1-3	2-5
Silica	1-10	1-7	trace	trace	1-5	1-7	9-20
Total of Solid Constituents	25 1-3	18 1-5	7	19 2-5	14 3-4	15	3 1-50
Gases	....	Free Carbonic Acid			....	....	....
Degree of Fahrenheit	50°2	56°		48°3	41°3	43°	....

Dr. Thomas G. Horn was a Colorado Springs physician who was impressed with the remedial value of Colorado's climate, air, and mineral springs, and he published articles promoting these features. In 1876, Dr. Horn traveled throughout Colorado on the governor's behalf, analyzing the springs of the state. In a publication presented to the Colorado Medical Society in 1877, entitled "Mineral Springs of Colorado," he described mineral water as a water which holds in solution different saline and gaseous substances. "A 'Mineral Water' then, in the medical acceptation of the term, is one which, by virtue of its ingredients, whether mineral, organic, gaseous or the principle of heat, is especially applicable to the treatment of disease." He warned that "like patent medicines, they are highly recommended for all diseases that humanity is heir to, while ignorance prevails as to their composition," and suggested that while "they *do* contain elements unknown to the profession, they are in no way more so than any of our best remedies of the present day." [28]

In 1913, Professor Herman Schlundt from the Department of Chemistry of the University of Missouri made his extensive study of various mineral waters throughout Colorado. The springs of Manitou showed a high degree of radioactivity, with the Shoshone Spring containing the highest amount of any of the 250 analyzed mineral springs in the state. This study created much excitement, due to the 1898 discovery by Marie and Pierre Curie that radium was useful in the treatment of cancer. [29]

Dr. Basil Creighton was another early Manitou physician who placed great value on the medical uses of the mineral springs. The *Chicago Medical Recorder* of

September 1915 published an article written by Dr. Creighton entitled "Manitou Springs," in which he discussed the mineral ingredients of the springs and their effects upon the body.

Sodium chloride adds to taste, promotes tissue change and increases the property some fluids possess of passing through membranes. Sodium sulphate and the magnesium salts are laxative. Ferrous bicarbonate is astringent, tonic and stimulant to blood formation. Precipitated iron is iron after it has been thrown down out of solution by contact with air, light and change in temperature. Calcium salts aid in body repair and are antiseptic to the extent of counteracting fermentation. Sodium bicarbonate is solvent to albumen. The combined alkalinity of these salts is soothing to mucous membranes, favors increased alkalinity of the blood and is anti-acid as well as corrective to hyperacid secretions of the stomach.

In the system, uric acid compounds, sugar, and other products of perverted metabolism are decomposed by the action of the mineral waters and the tendency to induce the normal elaboration of enzymes and ferments.

Radio-active emanations have energizing and vivifying qualities which are stimulating to cell activity. They endow fluid particles with active motility, thus promoting rapid absorption.

Carbonic acid gas, likewise radio-active, is powerfully stimulating internally through the direct chemical, physical, mechanical and reflex effects which it induces. [30]

Functional disorders of the stomach, gastric ulcers, and "such systemic diseases as diabetes, incipient Bright's engorgements of the liver, the anaemies, and conditions termed the uric acid diathesis" were some of the ailments listed in this article that would benefit through the drinking of the mineral water. Because imbibing the water would counteract hyperacidity and cleanse the mucous membranes of the stomach, Dr. Creighton stated that "in cancer of the stomach, only relief, due to cleanliness, may be expected." He felt that warmed mineral water was "effective in catarrhal conditions of the nose and throat." And he recommended bathing to be effective in cases of "obesity, gout, the neuroses, neurasthenia, gastritis, icterus, the various forms of rheumatism, sub-acute arthritis, incipient Bright's disease and incipient arterio-sclerosis." [31]

Dr. Creighton ended his paper with this paragraph:

The array of hygienic factors in this picturesque spot, amid a scenic environment that is grand, is so great and their quantity and quality is such that the use of mineral waters at Manitou is unusually effective and favorably influences a greater variety of diseased conditions than any known watering place or health resort. [32]

During the 1800s, the word "springs" was a drawing card that meant health resort. "Manitou" was the original name given this health resort, but sometime between 1872 and 1885 the word "Springs" was added. In 1885, the city officials dropped the

"Springs," and in 1891 the United States Board of Geographical Names accepted "Manitou" as the official title. The city of Colorado Springs capitalized on Manitou's springs and used the word in its official title. This was a source of bitterness between the two towns for many years. In November 1935, after much effort, the town clerk of Manitou Springs received a certificate from the Secretary of State, James M. Carr, stating that the official name of the town was *Manitou Springs.*

The most essential establishment at a spa is a bath house to utilize the waters externally through supervised bathing. According to an article that appeared in *Out West* on August 15, 1872, the first bath house had been constructed by the Colorado Springs Company. This was a long, narrow building containing five or six baths, located along the banks of Fountain Creek near the Shoshone Spring. The water for this bath house was piped from the Navajo Spring, and furnaces were installed to heat the cold mineral water. Dr. Boswell Anderson, who came to Manitou because of his consumption, was the physician in charge.

Dr. Boswell Anderson, wounded in the lung during the Civil War, was convinced that the injury was the cause of his tuberculosis. Aware of the importance of dry climate and sunshine as a treatment for the disease, he decided to come to Colorado. He accepted the position of bath house physician in Manitou, and arrived in 1872. By 1874 Dr. Anderson had recovered and moved to Colorado Springs to begin practicing medicine. He became one of El Paso County's most colorful and respected physicians.

Colorado Medical Society

The Manitou Bath House and Plunge was built in 1881 by the Manitou Mineral Water Bath and Park Company on the eastern edge of the Manitou Soda Springs Park, across from the original facility. The architecture of this $20,000 structure leaned to the Queen Anne style. There was little ornamentation, as the idea was to furnish a complete bath house in which visitors might avail themselves of the famous waters of Manitou. The building contained twenty bathrooms using either cold or heated mineral

The Colorado Springs Company built this first bath house in 1872. Mineral water from the Navajo Spring was piped to the bath house and furnaces were installed to heat the water. The building was located along Fountain Creek near the Shoshone Spring. The first bottling industry was located in one end of this building.

water from the Navajo Spring in the tubs, a 32- by 33-foot fresh water plunge, and thirty-two dressing closets.

The company published a flyer advertising this facility, claiming that "the SODA BATHS or a swim in the large plunge has been a luxurious experience not soon forgotten." It further declared that the popularity of this bath house had increased so much since opening that its fifty rooms were "taxed to . . . full capacity during the entire season." The same flyer guaranteed the patron nothing but pure mineral water in the baths. The price of the soda baths was fifty cents apiece, or ten for $4.50; the plunge was forty cents, with ten tickets costing $3.50. The advertisement described the uses of the baths as follows:

> These mineral baths are taken mainly as a luxurious method of cleanliness. They freely open the pores and render the skin soft and velvety. Their cosmetique action is admirable, and they are much resorted to for clearing and beautifying the complexion. In a high altitude and dry atmosphere the ordinary functions of the skin are largely in abeyance. To compensate for this peculiarity a bath should be taken at least once a week, and in very hot weather a daily bath is better. Frequent bathing is undoubtedly the best prophylactic for that low form of fever to which some persons are liable in mountainous regions. Where it is desired to remove from the system any poison like malaria, lead, rheumatism or other source

of disease, a hot bath should be taken (100 to 110 degrees Fahrenheit), but before leaving the tub, the bather should cool the water to about 95 degrees, and this should be followed by brisk rubbing with rough towels, and if reaction be slow, by some alcoholic preparation. As a tonic measure, a cool bath (60 to 95 degrees) should be taken. It is not desirable to remain in a bath longer than twenty minutes. Individuals who are particularly liable to taking cold after bathing may avoid this by bathing in the evening and retiring as soon as possible after it. [33]

Besides the baths and the plunge, this bath house offered spacious home-like parlors where music and games of various kinds and leading daily newspapers of the country were provided for the enjoyment and relaxation of the patrons. A room was set aside for a resident physician, who aided in the supervision of the baths. Several Manitou doctors saw fit to locate their offices in this building during its existence. It was torn down in the early 1900s.

Local History Collection, Pikes Peak Library

The greatest attraction offered by the Manitou Mineral Water Bath and Park Company was this Queen Anne style bath house, built in 1881.

Numerous attempts were made in the early 1900s to finance and build a modern bathing establishment for the proper administration of the health-giving baths. A group of Manitou citizens traveled to Hot Springs, Arkansas, to speak with W. C. Maurice, the country's foremost expert in the construction of bath houses, and to interest him in coming to Manitou to share his expertise in the founding of such a facility. World War I put an end to all building hopes, so the plans were shelved until after the war when Mr. Maurice consented to help the Manitou Springs Bath House Company build a bath house that would be equal in equipment to any other in the United States, and would compare favorably with any in Europe.

The committee decided that the Manitou Soda Springs Park, using the Manitou Soda Spring water, would be the logical location for their three-floor, Spanish-style, stucco building, which stands today. Because of his previous experience in bath house construction, Major John Fordyce of Little Rock, Arkansas, was hired to supervise the endeavor. The third story of the building contained private rooms with sanitary hospital beds to be used after bathing and rented for one night. The second floor was equipped with modern, white-tiled bathrooms and treatment rooms for men and women, while the first floor housed a restaurant, a beauty parlor, a barber shop, and other shops for the convenience of the visitors. This $350,000 masterpiece of engineering opened its doors on August 4, 1920.

Local History Collection, Pikes Peak Library

A modern, Spanish-style bath house replaced the pavilion of the Manitou Soda Spring.

The company advertised the bathrooms on the second floor to be well-ventilated, well-lighted, and equipped with needle and fan sprays, tubs, and showers; appliances for irrigation and internal baths; electric, hot-air, and vapor cabinets; and cold packs and compresses. Such devices were used in the administration of Turkish, Roman, Nauheim, Vichy, Maurice, continuous flow, and sitz baths, and Scotch douches. Every facility was provided to utilize the emanations from the radioactive ingredients found in the Manitou Soda Spring. Natural gases were separated from the head of the spring and used in the treatment of hay fever and asthma. This hydrotherapy department was supervised by trained therapists licensed by the United States government, and was under the direction of local physicians.

The massage department offered hand and electric vibratory treatments. The hand massages were administered by masseurs and masseuses of national reputation. The electrotherapeutic department was equipped with faradic, galvanic, sinusoidal, high frequency, static, and other currents, with alpine, violet, Bier, and other rays and lights.

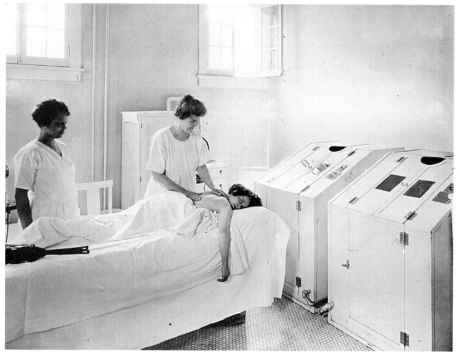

Dr. L. L. Williams Collection

This photo shows a masseuse giving a manual massage, the price for which was $2.00. The steel cabinets on the right were electric sweat boxes which produced a dry heat; the patient sat on a seat inside with her head through the hole on top.

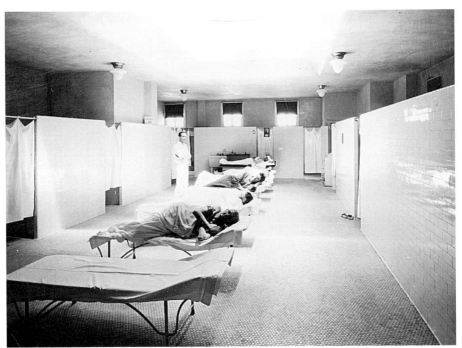

The tubs were located behind the curtains of the men's bathroom. The bathers relaxed on cots after taking hot baths under the supervision of a trained attendant.

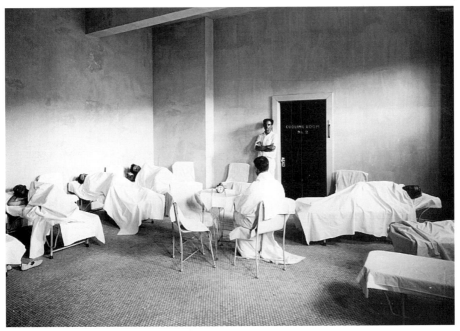

After their hot baths, the bathers were taken to a cooling room where their body temperatures could return to normal. Identical facilities were provided for the women.

This testimonial was printed in an advertisement for the Manitou Baths:

> I have been a constant sufferer from neuritis for the past three years, and for the past three months suffered more than usual. During this time I have been under the care of physicians and have taken baths and osteopathic treatments three times a week at other resorts, but without perceptible benefit or relief from pain.
>
> On the opening of the Manitou Bath House, I commenced treatment, taking the soda baths and massage treatments from Professor Sholz, and after the first bath last Friday I received considerable benefit and went sixteen hours without noticing any pain whatever. After taking four baths, for the first time in months I was entirely free from pain. [34]

Another advertisement suggested that the Manitou Baths were a "special aid in the treatment of sciatica, neuritis, rheumatism, asthma, and abnormal blood pressure." [35] Visitors from all over the country took advantage of this form of treatment. The price of the Manitou Radio-Soda Bath was $1.25 for a single ticket, or ten tickets for $10.00. The hot mineral baths, consisting of a course of twenty-one baths, cost $20.00. For the Electric Cabinet Bath (steam bath), a single ticket was $1.50, with ten tickets priced at $12.50.

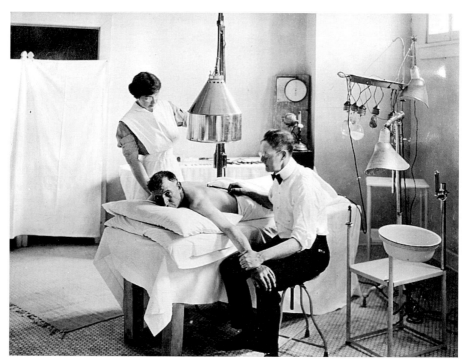

Dr. L. L. Williams Collection

Inside a treatment room of the Manitou Baths, an operator is using light therapy on this patient while an attendant monitors the pulse rate.

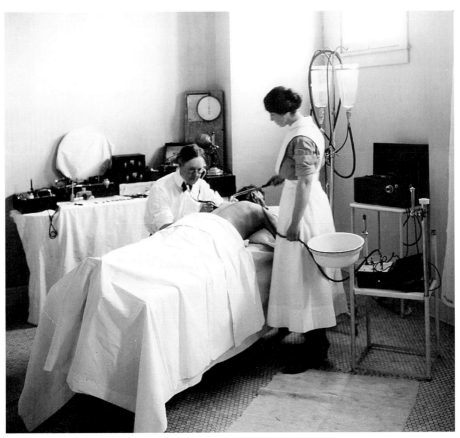

A form of electrotherapy is being administered to this patient while the attendant listens to the progress. The therapeutic department at the Manitou Baths was equipped to offer treatments using water, electricity, and light, all under the personal supervision of the best operators in the country.

In the 1950s the physical plant was used as a hotel and nursing home. It is interesting to note that in the middle sixties, new owners remodeled and reopened the building as a bath house, calling it the Manitou Spa. In 1966, it was approved as a rehabilitation agency for Medicare patients, who were able to use the mineral water baths, physical therapy, occupational therapy, and psychotherapy. They had to be under doctors' orders, and were carefully supervised by physical therapists and other personnel with nursing knowledge.

This facility has seen several owners who found it an economic and maintenance problem to operate it as a bath house. It is expensive to heat the cold mineral water for proper use in hydrotherapy and costly to keep the pipes and other equipment clear of mineral deposits that accumulate. Although the baths, which were on the second floor, have been removed, the shops and restaurant on the first floor are open to the public.

One industry that grew to magnificent proportions was that of bottling the mineral water for local as well as national consumption. Several attempts were made to bottle this water, but two companies surfaced to become the most successful.

The first bottling works was established in 1872 by the Colorado Springs Company at one end of the bath house on the banks of Fountain Creek. Later, a bottling shed was built next to the original building. This plant bottled sparkling table water from the Navajo Spring. A glass factory was built in Colorado City to produce the increasing number of bottles needed to contain this product called "Manitou."

Manitou Springs Historical Society

Out West, August 22, 1872, reported that 2,480 gallons of soda and iron water were consumed during the month of July. The article predicted that the bottling of the mineral water would become big business. The bottling industry began in 1872 in the long, narrow building below the bottling shed. As the demand for the table water increased, the industry moved into the shed seen behind the Shoshone Spring pagoda.

An advertisement that appeared in 1886 in the *Directory of Colorado Springs, Manitou Springs, and Colorado City* claimed this table water to be the "purest, most refreshing, and best tasting natural spring water." It went on to say that "like all waters strongly impregnated with carbonic acid gas, it aids digestion and is highly beneficial in dyspeptic and bilious conditions." [36] The price per case of fifty quart bottles that year was $7.50. Ten dollars would buy a case of one hundred pint bottles. At the time, the industry was owned by the Manitou Mineral Water Bath and Park Company.

So great was the demand for the bottled water that in 1890 a larger, three-story, redstone and frame building replaced the old shed. This plant cost $25,800 to construct. The new company began to bottle the Original "Manitou" Table Water and the Original "Manitou" Ginger Champagne, a ginger ale made from a secret recipe using ginger root.

Local History Collection, Pikes Peak Library

Original "Manitou" Table Water and Original "Manitou" Ginger Champagne were bottled here. This building, constructed in 1890, replaced the long, narrow building and shed that were the original bottling plants.

This new bottling plant was located just across Fountain Creek from the bath house.

The carbonation of these two products came from the natural carbonic acid gas of the Navajo Spring. This was an important factor featured in the advertisements. The sparkling, clear water was received in a hermetically sealed chamber located inside a spring house which protected the spring. Here the gas was separated from the water. As it ascended to the surface, the gas was collected in a heavy, plate-glass gathering hood located at the top of the spring chamber. Two tin pipes conducted the water and gas separately to the carbonating tank in the bottling plant, where they were again combined and directed into sterilized bottles at the same pressure as that found underground. Because of this process,

the company guaranteed the effervescence and freshness of the table water and ginger champagne, claiming that these were the only bottled beverages recharged in their own natural gas.

This building was the visitors' room of the Manitou Springs Mineral Water Company located at 930 Manitou Avenue, now the location of Patsy's Candies shop. The round, stone structure is the spring house of the Navajo Spring, from which the mineral water was piped to the bottling plant. The structure on the left is the pavilion of the Manitou Soda Spring.

An advertising booklet put out by the Manitou Springs Mineral Water Company spoke highly of the medicinal benefits of this clear, sparkling liquid as an aid to digestion and a general toning of the stomach, liver, and kidneys. It recommended that the water be mixed in equal proportions with milk and given to infants, to produce healthier, happier babies. It mentioned further that the table water was "soothing, allaying, and gently curative," and the beauty of it was that "it could do no harm." The following, still from this booklet, tells other uses:

> As a medicinal water and an active curative agent in all manner of disorders of the digestive and secretory organs the scope of Original "Manitou" Table Water is again most clearly defined. There are few cases of stomach trouble, whether they be chronic or acute, in which it may not be used with immediate relief and in many cases, permanent cure. Stubborn indigestion, stomachic fermentation, and super-acidity of any nature yield readily to consistent use of Original "Manitou," and it is the bitter enemy of a torpid liver. Kidney and bladder derangements are invariably benefited at once when this water is taken by the sufferer. Because of its splendid action on all the organs of elimination, it has decided value in any case of fever. [37]

This bottling venture was a victim of several unfortunate circumstances that led to its closing. The glass factory burned in 1906, making it necessary for the company to bear the expense of having bottles shipped from the East and then reshipping the filled bottles back to the Eastern markets. A new manager discontinued the bottling of the ginger champagne, a move which cost greatly in volume of sales. Another severe blow was a lawsuit involving the patent name of "Manitou." The judge ruled that a geographical name could not be used for one firm. The bottling plant was torn down in the mid-thirties.

The lawsuit was filed by the second successful bottling works, which used the name "Manitou" on the label of its own mineral water and ginger champagne. This competitor was the Ute Chief Mineral Water Company, established in 1897 by Jacob Schueler and his three sons, who operated this enterprise for forty-seven years. The bottling plant was located at the entrance to Ute Pass and used the water and carbonic acid gas from a number of nearby springs called the Ute Chief Manitou Group.

The Schueler family firmly believed in the medicinal benefits of their springs, and had the water analyzed to determine the mineral contents so that they could safely advertise the advantages of drinking their bottled products. Professor G. C. Tilden, of the Department of Chemistry at State School of Mines in Golden, Colorado, conducted this analysis, which was used in the adertising for the product.

Local History Collection, Pikes Peak Library

This photo of the Ute Chief Mineral Springs property appeared in the April 1907 issue of Rocky Mountain Resources. *The white building on the right was the original bottling plant, which burned in 1947.*

The medicinal value of these waters is due in great part to the Salts of Lime Magnesia they contain. Waters containing Carbonate of Soda are alkaline in reaction, and are found valuable in the treatment of disorders involving abnormal or acid secretions, as dyspepsia, especially when accompanied by acidity of the stomach. They act as diuretics and have been found valuable in the treatment of diabetes. A careful analysis of Ute Chief Manitou Water proves the absence of Nitrites, Nitrates, Free and Albumenoid Ammonia, and other substances of organic origin, which, when present render a water unfit for drinking purposes. The Ute Chief Manitou Water is highly charged with Carbonic Acid Gas, which has its origin in a natural source at the spring. This water will no doubt find favor as a table water, as it has all the chemical and physical properties which render a water valuable as such.[38]

The Ute Chief Mineral Water Company advertised its water "as an appetizer, as an aid to digestion, and as a remedy for stomach disorders" because it contained "those mineral properties necessary for the aid of nature and the supplying and proper balancing of the body chemicals." The company suggested the "Ute Chief Manitou Water is highly efficacious in the treatment of Rheumatism and all Kidney Diseases, for Bright's Disease, Diabetes, Torpid Liver, Malaria, Dyspepsia, Nervous Prostration and Insomnia,"[39] and claimed the water to be "Nature's Big Medicine Man."[40]

Manitou Springs Historical Society

The Ute Chief Mineral Water Company was proud of its products and advertised widely. It declared that the springs were capable of producing five thousand fifty-quart cases of mineral water every twenty-four hours.

The two bottling companies were similar in many ways. Their products contained the soda water of the nearby springs and were charged with the natural carbonation from their source; they exercised rigid sanitary precautions; they claimed great medical benefits from the drinking of their products; and they spent a great deal of effort and money to advertise their beverages.

The railroad was essential to the survival of the bottling industry of Manitou. Freight cars loaded with table water and ginger champagne delivered all over the United States. Seventy thousand bottles were shipped out from June to December of 1886; this number increased to two hundred thousand by 1892, and to four million in 1893. As many as sixty carloads were counted on one local freight line. The railroad also brought new bottles from Eastern markets. As the trains gradually discontinued their runs to Manitou, the outside market became more difficult to reach, perhaps a factor in the decline of this industry.

The 1945 Ute Chief bottling plant is still standing. Several owners have unsuccessfully attempted to restore the operations. Presently the new owner is planning to develop a micro brewery that will bottle beer as well as root beer, cream soda, champagne ale, and mineral water. The building is being renovated to become an upscale brew pub. The owner hopes to put the tall cement bottle back on its original site, across Manitou Avenue from the bottling plant.

This cement bottle was placed over the Ute Chief Gusher with the water erupting over the top. It was at one time an impressive tourist attraction and an advertising gimic for the Ute Chief Mineral Water Company.

Local History Collection, Pikes Peak Library

Manitou Springs Historical Society

The original Ute Chief bottling plant, built in 1897, was destroyed by fire. It was replaced by a modern facility in 1945, the inside of which is seen in this photograph.

A **physician whose eloquence** demonstrated his love for Manitou and helped promote it as a health resort was Dr. Basil B. Creighton (1864 – 1966), who came to the Pikes Peak region in 1893 with active tuberculosis.[41] Upon his arrival, he found nature to be "in her mildest mood," supplying Manitou with year-round tonic climate, unsurpassed scenery, and "mineralized waters of soda and iron, freshly blended, finely filtered, a nectar fit for the Gods," and certainly "a place to regain the loss of that most precious of all gifts — health." These thoughts were expressed by Dr. Creighton in an article published in the *Chicago Medical Recorder* in 1915.[42] The doctor also described this spa and its therapeutic advantages in a brochure he called "Manitou Springs and the Springs of Manitou." He was a testimonial to these beliefs as he lived to the age of 102, the oldest licensed physician in Colorado.

Creighton and Forde Family Files

Dr. Basil B. Creighton

Dr. Creighton entered Ohio Medical College in 1888, graduating with honors in 1892. He was the first intern at the Good Samaritan Hospital in his home town of Cincinnati, Ohio, and during his internship he contracted tuberculosis. His illness led him to Manitou where two of his brothers were already residing. He became the camp physician in Cripple Creek during the gold rush years and assisted the Sisters of Mercy in establishing a hospital in this thriving gold town.

Upon his return to Manitou in 1895 he again worked with the Sisters of Mercy in helping them found Montcalme Sanitarium, where he was on duty every day for seventeen years. He served as Manitou's city physician for many years. He was instrumental in bringing the Sisters of Charity from the Good Samaritan Hospital in Cincinnati to Colorado Springs to operate Glockner Sanatorium. In addition to practicing medicine for sixty years in Manitou, he owned and operated a drugstore.

Dr. Creighton's philosophy of medicine was that doctors never cure anyone — nature does the curing and doctors only help. He delivered countless babies, never losing either baby or mother; he successfully nursed all his patients through the 1917 influenza epidemic. He cared for many Indian, Chinese, and Japanese patients who lived in Manitou, and often his payment was an Indian rug or china. Dr. Creighton recalled that his first patient was the president of the Rock Island Railroad.

He was known as the "walking doctor." He firmly believed that he owed his long life to this form of exercise. He shunned the horse and buggy and purchased only one automobile. This ownership lasted three days — his chauffeur wrecked it and Dr. Creighton never bought another.

His mind was always active and he kept it nourished by constant reading, particularly in the fields of science and mathematics. The doctor was fascinated by space and astronomy, and prior to 1950 he predicted that man would walk on the moon sometime after 1971. In 1959, when he was 85, he took up reading and typing braille so that he could help one of his daughters prepare her lessons for the Colorado School for the Deaf and Blind where she taught. At age 86 he learned Russian, stating that "if those fellows ever come over here, I want to be able to tell them what I think of them." [43]

A health seeker who contributed a great deal to the history of Manitou medicine was Father Jean Baptist Francolon. He was born in France, to a family of wealth and nobility, and educated in the diplomatic field at the best schools of Paris, but his religious convictions led him into the priesthood. Upon the completion of his theological training, he was assigned to the see of Santa Fe in the United States as secretary to Archbishop Lamy, and, in 1883, was placed in charge of the Santa Cruz mission. At this time he used his influence to secure the right-of-way through Indian lands for the Denver and Rio Grande Western Railroad. Father Francolon's earlier training served him well in obtaining this land, and it kept him active on occasional diplomatic missions for the French government.

His career with the church and his outside projects finally wore him to the point of poor health. He decided to come to Manitou after hearing of the climate and the curative powers of the waters. In 1892, he was assigned to the church of Our Lady of Perpetual Help. He purchased a large plot of land above the church on Capitol Hill Avenue and built his first home above Miramont Castle on the site of the existing upper parking lot.

In July of 1895 he generously donated this home to the Sisters of Mercy, who used it as a sanitarium they called Montcalme. Montcalme Sanitarium was opened to the public on August 1, 1895. This project was launched by Reverend Mother Baptist from Denver and three local Sisters of Mercy, with the help of Dr. Creighton. Their goal was to serve persons whose physicians recommended rest and the benefits of a change of climate. A majority of the patients were afflicted with some form of tuberculosis, but their cases were not acute in nature. In 1896, Montcalme Sanitarium cared for 195 patients and invalids.

Meanwhile, with the aid of a local building contractor, Angus Gillis, Father Francolon immediately began to design a new residence that may have resembled the château on the Francolon estate in France. Many hours were spent at the Gillis home, at which time the Father would explain what he wanted and Angus would draw the type of architecture described. If the Father approved, they would go on with the next description; if not, Angus would work on the design until it pleased Father Francolon. This is how the two came up with a skillful blend of nine different architectural styles. The castle was started by the Gillis Brothers Construction Company of Manitou about 1894 and completed in January 1897. Father called his home "Miramont," and it was located adjacent to the Montcalme Sanitarium. This unique structure has been a tourist attraction through the years.

The twenty-eight-room home in the foreground is Miramont Castle. The arch leads to Montcalme Sanitarium, Father Francolon's original home, which he later donated to the Sisters of Mercy.

Francolon's mother joined him in his new home, which was constructed of Manitou greenstone and other native materials. Miramont was furnished lavishly, complete with paintings by the old Italian masters and tapestries dating back to Isabella of Castile. A grand opening was held on February 22, 1897, and the elite of Manitou, Colorado Springs, and Denver were invited. It was a costume ball honoring George Washington's birthday, and a fund-raising project for the Manitou library. The evening was spent dancing the minuet and cotillion in costumes dating to the days of Washington and Adams. All in attendance and those who observed from the outside were impressed with the grandeur of the evening, described in the *Colorado Springs Republican*:

> The brilliant decoration of the French and national flags, costly draperies and paintings, cut flowers and potted plants, the soulful strains of music and the merry dancing in the dress of a hundred years ago presented a dreamland picture such as has never before been witnessed in the beautiful little hamlet at the foot of the great white mountain.[44]

In 1900 Father Francolon left Manitou unexpectedly, never to return. The Sisters of Mercy who operated the nearby Montcalme Sanitarium took over the castle-like residence and operated it, too, as a sanitarium. In April 1904, the Sisters succeeded in purchasing Miramont. The title to the property had been vested in a Mother House of the Catholic Church in London, causing great effort on the part of the Sisters of Mercy to consummate the purchase. The price paid remains obscure.

The entire complex became known as Montcalme Sanitarium. The Sisters launched a campaign to advertise their enlarged facility in newspapers and periodicals around the country. In the *Colorado Springs Evening Telegraph* dated January 1, 1906, the advertisement read as follows:

> Nestling almost at the foot of Pike's Peak following the bend of the hills, lies the MONTCALME SANITARIUM, one of the most picturesque and finest equipped places of this kind to be found anywhere. . . . This institution is elegantly furnished and possessed of every convenience known for the care of its patients. As Manitou is Nature's Greatest Sanatoria so is Montcalme Colorado's Greatest Sanitarium. The management is in the hands of the Sisters of Mercy, which is in itself the greatest of all guarantees that all patients receive the best of care and will be gently nursed back to robust health. [45]

At the time of the purchase, Miramont was to be remodeled and enlarged to provide rooms for two hundred patients. Dr. J. W. Geiermann, formerly of the Kneipp Sanitarium in Rome, Indiana, encouraged the Sisters to offer the Kneipp "water cure" in their institution, and he loaned them the funds for this purpose. This cure was a form of therapy developed by a Catholic priest in Germany, and it became a popular treatment in this country. It consisted of regular barefoot exercises in the sunshine and fresh air on dew-moistened grass and on snow, and it emphasized walking properly and eating a balanced diet. This program did not prove successful and was discontinued in 1907.

The original Montcalme structure above Miramont burned in November of 1907. The Sisters succeeded in saving all the patients from the burning building. All but the lower floor was destroyed, resulting in $25,000 to $50,000 damage. Despite the strong winds, the fire department was able to save Miramont. An arch framing the steps that led to Montcalme bore the name of the sanitarium; after the fire, the Sisters relocated

Local History Collection, Pikes Peak Library

Miramont Castle became Montcalme Sanitarium after the 1907 fire.

this arch in front of Miramont. Thus for the next sixty-nine years Father Francolon's castle was known as Montcalme.

The history of Montcalme from the time of the fire was one of financial problems. The remaining "castle structure" served in a limited way as a sanitarium and was closed in 1928. The Sisters of Mercy used it as a retreat from then until 1946 when it was sold to private individuals who converted the building into apartment units.

In 1976, it was purchased by the Manitou Springs Historical Society, which succeeded in getting the building listed on the National Register as a historic place under its original name, Miramont. Through grants, donations, and hard work, it has been remodeled to appear once again as Father Francolon designed it. The society operates it as a museum, open to the public for tours.

Local History Collection, Pikes Peak Library

This drawing shows the proposed addition to Montcalme Sanitarium as envisioned by the Sisters of Mercy. The upper portion is the one hundred-room addition, estimated to cost $150,000. It failed to become a reality.

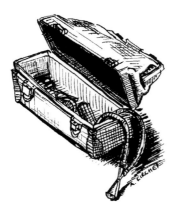

A perfect example of a health seeker was Dr. Henry M. Ogilbee (1859–1939), and this is his story as told by his daughter, Mrs. Jean M. Campbell.

After his graduation from medical school at Western Reserve University in Cleveland, Ohio, Dr. Ogilbee set up practice in a small town in that state. After a break in health, he informed his wife that he was going to travel to every state until he found a climate that agreed with him, as he firmly believed climate had a great influence on one's physical condition. He started in the northwest, journeying down the coast and making his way around to Florida. From Florida he wrote to his family that nowhere had he felt better, so he was about to return home. Remembering how well he had felt while on his honeymoon in Manitou, Colorado, he decided to spend some time here before ending his search. Needless to say, his quest ended at the spa of Manitou, where he remained until his death at the age of eighty-three.

Jean M. Campbell

Dr. Henry M. Ogilbee

Dr. Ogilbee's practice in Manitou lasted forty-seven years. He was especially busy in the summer caring for the health-seeking tourists. He had many referrals from the Cliff House, as he was a personal friend of the proprietor and his home was one door east of this hotel. He was the first Cogway Railway physician. It was very popular for the tourists to make the trip up Pikes Peak, but altitude got the best of many of them and fainting was a common occurrence. Dr. Ogilbee would travel to the top and care for the victims. This job didn't last long as the doctor soon realized that it took all day to go up and back, when he was needed by his patients in Manitou.

Because his own faith in climate was so strong, he felt the medical profession didn't fully appreciate the effect of climate on health. Dr. Ogilbee believed that the waters of the Shoshone Spring had great medicinal qualities, and he recommended that certain patients drink the waters.

The doctor and his wife were parents of four children. In addition to the time required by his medical practice, his family, and his love for animals, he found time to establish the second bank in Manitou and was the chairman of its board of directors until his death. He was also on the library board and is mentioned in the book *Who's Who in Colorado*.

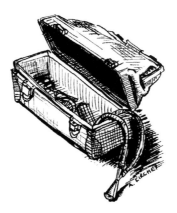

Dr. L. H. Beck arrived in Manitou in 1899 to practice medicine and surgery. He received his Bachelor of Arts as salutatorian of the class of 1895 from Heidelberg University in Tiffin, Ohio, and prior to his advanced education he taught in the public schools in this, his native state. After entering Ohio Medical University in Columbus, he was forced by poor health to seek a better climate; he came to Colorado and finished his training for his career at Gross Medical College of Denver, where he received his degree in April 1898.

Local History Collection, Pikes Peak Library

Dr. L. H. Beck

Dr. Beck was an esteemed member of the El Paso County Medical Society, the Colorado Medical Society, the American Medical Association, and the American Academy of Medicine. In 1912 he was one of twenty-five delegates appointed to represent the latter organization in the Fifteenth International Congress of Hygiene and Demography in Washington, D. C. Dr. Beck enjoyed a growing practice in Manitou. In 1900 he married Minnie D. Zimmer, and the two occupied a respected position in the social life of this resort village. [46]

From time immemorial, the mineral springs of Manitou Springs have enjoyed a reputation for their health-giving waters. The natural and drilled springs became an attraction that brought people from all over the world in search of health, rest, and recreation. Health and tourism became industries important to the economy of the little village, and the mineral springs were the backbone of its survival.

Manitou reached its glory in the 1890s and early 1900s. As a spa, Manitou was unequaled, and physicians took advantage of the mineral waters for the treatment of certain diseases. With the concerns brought on by two world wars and the depression of the thirties, the invalid found that it was more convenient and less expensive to purchase a patent medicine than to pack bags and travel to a spa. Physicians began to make use of the miracle drugs and modern medical technology. These are contributing factors that led to the decline of the health industry of the "Saratoga of the West."

The trains gradually discontinued their runs to Manitou Springs. The fifty springs and geysers were reduced to only a few operable. The hotels that were not destroyed by fire were in disrepair and some even condemned to be torn down. The white stucco spa went through several owners. The Manitou Springs Mineral Water Company's redstone and frame bottling plant was torn down, while the Ute Chief bottling plant boarded its windows. Montcalme, the village's only sanitarium, became an apartment house.

The glorious days of this sacred watering place became history almost forgotten in the rush of today's technical world, but the rich heritage of Manitou Springs's past is too valuable to be lost and is essential for the survival of this community — a fact realized by many of her citizens.

In 1977 Miramont was placed on the National Register as a historic place and became a museum open to the public by the Manitou Springs Historical Society. This act marked the beginning of an exciting restoration phase in Manitou Springs's history. In 1980 the Manitou Springs City Council enacted a preservation ordinance which established a Historic Preservation Commission and a local preservation district. The commission was successful in getting Manitou Springs placed on the National Register of Historic Places in 1983. The Manitou Springs Development Company, the Mineral Springs Foundation, Manitou Springs Chamber of Commerce, and numerous other organizations have all contributed to the effort of preserving Manitou's glorious past. Many residents and outside investors have purchased, remodeled, and restored homes, hotels, and businesses that were unique in their architectural design and their historic background. Much of the preservation work is done by dedicated volunteers who have a strong interest in the history of this village. Manitou Springs's past is becoming an exciting addition to the future, and memories of the "Saratoga of the West" can be recalled with each visit.

Courtesy, Colorado Historical Society

The junction of Manitou and Canon Avenues creates a wedge of land where the bottling works and bath house once stood. The town clock remains as a reminder of the past.

AFTERWORD

The Mineral Springs Foundation was created in 1987. This group of volunteers is working to restore the major springs and to recall their history for the enjoyment of visitors and the citizens of Manitou. To encourage the drinking of the waters and to assure the public that the waters are safe to drink, the foundation contracts for a monthly water quality check with the El Paso County Department of Heath and Environment.

The springs of Manitou still contain minerals that are thought by some to be useful for the maintenance of good health. To provide information on the mineral contents of the springs, the Manitou Springs Foundation hired the Colorado Springs Utilities Water Quality Laboratory and Industrial Laboratories of Denver to analyze the waters of the four natural and four drilled springs that have been restored. The following table shows the minerals and the amounts found in the four natural springs in 1990 and 1993. Mineral content information on the other springs is available through the Manitou Springs Chamber of Commerce. It is interesting to compare the mineral ingredients in this report with those in Professor Loew's shown on page 41.[47]

Mineral Springs Foundation Lists of Mineral Content

Cheyenne Spring			7/25/90
Alkalinity	HCO_3	2095	ppm
Calcium	Ca	408	ppm
Chloride	Cl	220	ppm
Chromium	Cr	1.1	ppb
Copper	Cu	73	ppb
Fluoride	F	3.03	ppm
Magnesium	Mg	69	ppm
Manganese	Mn	1500	ppb
Potassium	K	66	ppm
Silica	S10	43	ppm
Sodium	Na	371	ppm
Sulfate	SO_4	189	ppm
Zinc	Zn	130	ppb
Total Disp So	TDS	2820	ppm

Navajo Spring			6/25/93
Alkalinity	HCO_3	1980	ppm
Calcium	Ca	385	ppm
Chloride	Cl	220	ppm
Chromium	Cr	.5	ppb
Copper	Cu	5	ppb
Fluoride	F	2.98	ppm
Magnesium	Mg	69	ppm
Manganese	Mn	40	ppm
Potassium	K	63.2	ppm
Silica	S10	42.6	ppm
Sodium	Na	361	ppm
Sulfate	SO_4	185	ppm
Zinc	Zn	110	ppb
Total Disp So	TDS	2600	ppm

Ute Chief Spring			9/14/93
Alkalinity	HCO_3	1125	ppm
Calcium	Ca	326	ppm
Chloride	Cl	110	ppm
Copper	Cu	2	ppm
Fluoride	F	2.93	ppm
Magnesium	Mg	49	ppm
Manganese	Mn	20	ppb
Potassium	K	19	ppm
Silica	S10	22	ppm
Sodium	Na	120	ppm
Zinc	Zn	74	ppb
Total Disp So	TDS	1460	ppm

Iron Spring			9/14/93
Alkalinity	HCO_3	1402	ppm
Calcium	Ca	136	ppm
Chloride	Cl	190	ppm
Chromium	Cr	1.2	ppb
Copper	Cu	31	ppb
Fluoride	F	4.44	ppm
Magnesium	Mg	32	ppm
Manganese	Mn	710	ppb
Potassium	K	80	ppm
Silica	S10	80	ppm
Sodium	Na	531	ppm
Sulfate	SO_4	219	ppm
Zinc	Zn	49	ppb
Total Disp So	TDS	2190	ppm

Mineral Water Recipes

These recipes are provided through the courtesy of The Mineral Springs Foundation.

Manitou Lemonade   1 gallon

2 large cans frozen lemonade concentrate
3 quarts chilled mineral water from your favorite spring (bubbly is best)
Dilute to your taste

The popular springs are Twin and Ute Chief
The most popular powder mix is Country Time

Iced Tea

Make strong tea base
You can add extras such as mint, lemon, orange, or sweetener
Add to chilled mineral water and ice
Dilute to perfection

Sangria Blanca   2 quarts

Blend
3 ½ cups dry white wine
½ cup orange liqueur or orange juice concentrate
½ cup brandy or apple juice
¼ cup sweetener
2 cups or more chilled mineral water
Garnish with lime, orange, or apple slices

Cranberry Cooler   1 gallon

1 large can frozen cranberry juice concentrate
1 large can lemonade concentrate
1 large can orange juice concentrate
10 cups (2 ½ pints) chilled mineral water
1 large bottle ginger ale, chilled if desired

White Fantasy Punch   2 quarts

½ cup frozen grapefruit juice concentrate, warmed
½ cup honey
Add 2 quarts chilled mineral water
Pour over 1 pint softened pineapple sherbet

ENDNOTES

1. L. Edwin Smith, *Manitou, The Gitche Spirit of the Red Man* (Colorado Springs, Colorado: Out West Printing and Stationery Company, 1919), pp. 23–25.

2. "Manitou, Colorado: At the Foot of Pikes Peak," travel folder, n.d., Special Collections and Archives, The Colorado College Library.

3. LeRoy R. Hafen, ed., *Colorado and Its People*, 4 vols. (New York: Lewis Historical Publishing Co., Inc., 1948), 2:387.

4. Rueben Gold Thwaites, Part 3 of James' Account of S. H. Long's Expedition, 1819–1820, *Early Western Travels, 1748–1846*, 32 vols. (Cleveland, Ohio: The Arthur H. Clarke Company, 1905), 16:12.

5. "Manitou — Opening of the Season and Its Principal Hotel," *Facts* 3, no. 29 (23 April 1898):4.

6. *Rufus B. Sage, His Letters and Papers, 1836–1847*, vol. 2, with Introduction, Biographical Sketch and Notes by LeRoy R. Hafen and Ann W. Hafen. *The Far West and the Rockies Historical Series, 1820–1875*, 15 vols. (Glendale, California: The Arthur H. Clarke Company, 1956), 5:75.

7. Ibid., pp. 75–76.

8. George F. Ruxton, *Adventures in Mexico and the Rocky Mountains, 1846-1847* (London: J. Murray, 1847), p. 253.

9. Ibid., pp. 254–57.

10. Fitz Hugh Ludlow, *The Heart of the Continent* (New York: Hurd and Houghton, 1870), p. 178.

11. William A. Bell, "Story of Manitou," talk before the Village Improvement Society, August 1896, Special Collections and Archives, The Colorado College Library.

12. Ibid.

13. *Out West* 1, no. 12, 20 June 1872, p. 8.

14. Rhoda Davis Wilcox, *The Bells of Manitou* (Colorado Springs, Colorado: Little London Press, 1973), p. 16.

15. Among these was Dr. Solly's *The Health Resorts of Colorado Springs and Manitou: Also a Prize Article, Descriptive of Scenery, Resources, etc. by Mrs. Simeon J. Dunbar* (Colorado Springs, Colorado: Gazette Publishing Company, n.d.).

16. The sanitariums established during the time period discussed in this book may have used either "Sanitarium" or "Sanatorium" in their official names. The author has chosen to use the former spelling throughout her text.

17. *Colorado Springs Weekly Gazette*, 6 November 1875.

18. Samuel Edwin Solly, *Manitou, Colorado, Its Mineral Waters and Climate*, 2d ed. (Colorado Springs, Colorado: Gazette Publishing Company, 1882), p. 21.

19. Ibid., p. 23.

20. S. K. Hooper, *Manitou* (Cincinnati, Ohio: The A. H. Pugh Publishing Co., 1888), pp. 56–57.

21. "The Tourist's Delight, The Invalid's Haven, Manitou Springs, Colorado: A Short Treatise on Its Incomparable Climate, Its Scenic Beauty and Its Advantages as a Place for a Brief Sojourn or Permanent Residence" (Manitou Springs, Colorado: The Manitou Journal, 1891).

22. "Manitou," *The Manitou Item* 1, no. 1, 27 May 1882.

23. "Manitou," *Facts* 4, no. 42 (22 July 1899):8–10.

24. "Manitou Springs, Colorado, 'The Scenic Center' at the Foot of Pikes Peak," Manitou Business Men's Association, travel folder, n.d., Special Collections and Archives, The Colorado College Library.

25. Hooper, *Manitou*, p. 55.

26. *Colorado Springs Sun*, 1 August 1974, p. 24, clipping, Local History Collection, Pikes Peak Library.

27. Hooper, *Manitou*, p. 58.

28. Thomas G. Horn, "Report on the Mineral Springs of Colorado," paper presented to the Colorado Medical Society, reprinted in the *Second Annual Report of the State Board of Health of Colorado*, issued in Denver, 1878, pp. 47, 52.

29. Herman Schlundt, "The Radioactivity of Some Colorado Springs," *The Journal of Physical Chemistry* 18, no. 7 (November 1914):664.

30. Basil B. Creighton, "Manitou Springs," *Chicago Medical Recorder*, September 1915, pp. 10–11.

31. Ibid., p. 12.

32. Ibid.

33. "The Manitou Soda Springs Bathing Establishment," The Manitou Mineral Water Company, advertising brochure, n.d., Special Collections and Archives, The Colorado College Library.

34. "The Manitou Baths," The Manitou Springs Bath House Company, advertising brochure, n.d., Special Collections and Archives, The Colorado College Library.

35. "The Manitou Baths, A Special Aid in the Treatment of Sciatica, Neuritis, Rheumatism, Asthma and Abnormal Blood Pressure," The Manitou Springs Bath House Company, advertising brochure, n.d., Western History Department, Denver Public Library.

36. *Directory of Colorado Springs, Manitou Springs, and Colorado City, 1886* (Colorado Springs, Colorado: S. N. Francis, 1886).

37. "Original 'Manitou,' 'The Peer of Table Waters,'" The Manitou Springs Mineral Water Company, advertising brochure, n.d., Special Collections and Archives, The Colorado College Library.

38. "Ute Chief Manitou," Ute Chief Mineral Water Company, advertising brochure, n.d., provided by Elsie Schueler.

39. Ibid.

40. "Waters of Life," unpublished article, n.d., provided by Elsie Schueler.

41. Information about Dr. Creighton was obtained through interviews with the Creighton and Forde families and from the family files.

42. Creighton, "Manitou Springs," pp. 1–4.

43. "Walking Fan Alive at 101," *The Denver Post*, 10 October 1965, p. 42.

44. Description reprinted in "The Magnificent Castle of Manitou Springs," *The Denver Post*, Empire Magazine, 13 June 1976.

45. *Colorado Springs Evening Telegraph*, 1 January 1906, p. 18.

46. *The History of Colorado*, Deluxe supplement (Chicago: S. J. Clarke Publishing Company, 1918), pp. 393–94.

47. City of Colorado Springs, Colorado Springs Water Quality Lab Reports, 25 July 1990, 25 June 1993.

SELECTED BIBLIOGRAPHY

Articles and Books

Bell, Cara Georgina Whitmore. "A Journal of Cara Georgina Whitmore Bell about Her Early Married Life in America, 1872-1876." Mimeographed. N.d. Special Collections and Archives, The Colorado College Library.

Buckman, George Rex. *Colorado Springs and Its Scenic Environs.* 2d ed. New York: Trow Print; Colorado Springs, Colorado, 1893.

Copp, Shirley. *Miramont Castle, a Brief History and Walking Tour: Descriptions of Castle Rooms.* Manitou Springs: Manitou Springs Historical Society, 1993.

"Cures Cancer — Manitou Springs." Newspaper clipping, date cut off. Local History Collection, Pikes Peak Library.

Daniels, Bettie, and McConnell, Virginia. *The Springs of Manitou.* Denver: Sage Books, 1964.

Fetler, John. *The Pikes Peak People.* The Story of America's Most Popular Mountain. Caldwell, Idaho: The Caxton Printers, Ltd., 1966.

"The Fountain Colony — Villa La Font." *Daily Central City Register*, 25 June 1871, p. 4.

History of the Sisters of Mercy in Colorado, 1882–1916. Compiled by Sister M. Nicholas Orr. N.d. Found at Mercy Hospital, Denver.

Ingersoll, Ernest. *The Crest of the Continent.* Chicago: R. R. Donnelley and Sons, 1885.

McIlrath, Clemma. "History of Cliff House." N.d. Local History Collection, Pikes Peak Library.

Murphy, Bradford. "Samuel Edwin Solly, M.D., 1845–1906." Copied for Colorado Medical Society Historical Archives, 5 June 1965.

Roberts, Edward. *Colorado Springs and Manitou.* Chicago: R. R. Donnelley and Sons, 1883.

Rocky Mountain Resources. Industrial and Trade Review of the Rocky Mountain Region. Vol. 1, no. 6, April 1907.

Ruxton, George F. *Adventures in Mexico and the Rocky Mountains, 1846–1847.* London: J. Murray, 1847.

Schlundt, Herman. "The Radioactivity of Some Colorado Springs." *The Journal of Physical Chemistry* 18, no. 7, November 1914, p. 664.

Smith, L. Edwin. *Manitou, The Gitche Spirit of the Red Man.* Colorado Springs, Colorado: Out West Printing and Stationery Company, 1919.

Solly, Samuel Edwin. *Manitou, Colorado, Its Mineral Waters and Climate.* 2d ed. Colorado Springs, Colorado: Gazette Publishing Company, 1882.

Sprague, Marshall. *Newport in the Rockies: The Life and Good Times of Colorado Springs*. Rev. ed. Denver: Sage Books, 1964.

Warner, Louis H. *Archbishop Lamy; An Epoch Maker*. Santa Fe, New Mexico: Santa Fe New Mexican Publishing Company, 1936.

The Westerners. The 1967 Brand Book. Ed. Richard A. Ronzio, vol. 23. Boulder, Colorado: Johnson Publishing, 1968.

Wetherill, Horace G. "Three Colorado Pioneers. Samuel Edwin Solly." *Journal of the Outdoor Life*, Special Colorado number. New York: National Tuberculosis Association, Summer 1932, pp. 347–48.

Wilcox, Rhoda Davis. *The Bells of Manitou*. Colorado Springs, Colorado: Little London Press, 1973.

Zecha, C. J. "Manitou Castle Once Used by Mercy Nuns as Hospital." *Denver Catholic Register*, 3 January 1963, pp. 1–2.

Newspapers and Other Periodicals

Colorado Prospector
Colorado Springs Evening Telegraph
Colorado Springs Free Press
Colorado Springs Gazette
Colorado Springs Gazette Telegraph
Colorado Springs Sun
Colorado Springs Weekly Gazette
The Denver Post
Directory of Colorado Springs, Manitou Springs, and Colorado City
Facts
The Manitou Item
Mountain Sunshine
Out West
Pikes Peak Journal

Personal Interviews

Jean M. Campbell

Shirley Copp

Basil B. Creighton

Alfred H. Dwyer

Albert and Edwina Forde

Elsie Schueler

Mike Stanton

Additional information was obtained from Manitou files located in the following institutions:

Colorado Historical Society

Colorado Medical Society

Denver Public Library, Western History Department

Local History Collection, Pikes Peak Library

Manitou Springs Historical Society

Manitou Springs Public Library

Colorado Springs Pioneers Museum

Special Collections and Archives, The Colorado College Library